ARE THORESEN was born in Norway in 1952. A doctor of veterinary medicine, he has also studied anthroposophic medicine, homeopathy, acupuncture, osteopathy and agriculture. Since 1981 he has run a private holistic practise in Sandefjord, Norway, for the healing of small animals and horses, as well as people. He has lectured widely, specializing in veterinary acupuncture, and has published dozens of scholarly articles. In 1984 he started to treat cancer patients, both human and animals, and this work has been the focus of much of his recent research. He is the author of several books on complementary medicine that have been publi   ious languages.

CW01083553

Demons depicted on The Book of Wonders, *a late fourteenth century Arabic manuscript*

Demons
and Healing

The Reality of the Demonic Threat and the Doppelgänger
in the Light of Anthroposophy

Demonology, Christology and Medicine

Are Simeon Thoresen, DVM

TEMPLE LODGE

Temple Lodge Publishing Ltd.
Hillside House, The Square
Forest Row, RH18 5ES

www.templelodge.com

Published in English by Temple Lodge in 2018

Originally self-published in an earlier version under the title *Demons, Spiritual Medicine* via CreateSpace in 2017

This new edition has been re-edited and expanded in cooperation with the author by Temple Lodge Publishing. With thanks to Michael Allen for his editorial contribution

A CIP catalogue record for this book is available from the British Library

ISBN 978 1 912230 18 1

Cover by Morgan Creative featuring image © agsandrew
Typeset by DP Photosetting, Neath, West Glamorgan
Printed and bound by 4Edge Ltd., Essex

Dedicated to all who seek to heal and understand

Contents

Foreword

This book is an inquiry into anthroposophical medicine by the Norwegian acupuncturist and veterinarian Are Thoresen. The book is a personal testimony, revealing the different stages of the author's experiences in this field against the background of almost 40 years of therapeutic practice.

The central ideas of the book can be summarized as follows:

1) Anthroposophical medicine has to be thought of as part of a cosmic process. The practitioner does not deal with human beings or animals as distinct entities, but as interwoven with greater cosmic forces.
2) The universe is of a spiritual nature, of which the healer is also part.
3) The healer must acknowledge that the forces in the spiritual world are not only good. Evil spirits or demons also exist, and they are more numerous and have a greater significance than commonly acknowledged.
4) In the treatment of diseases, the power of Christ is the most important tool.
5) Finally, because the healer is part of a greater spiritual whole: he is a world healer.

The book arrives at a critical moment in the history of humankind. Today, we are witnessing the breakdown of an old worldview that has dominated modern philosophy and science since the Renaissance. This worldview is characterized by a materialistic and mechanistic understanding of man and the universe at all levels of society. This way of thinking has had some advantages in the past, not least with regard to technological innovations. However, just as it has its specific premises, it also has its limitations, which now have been pushed to their outmost bounds. Our civilization is facing challenges and problems that have been caused by the very same thinking, which in order to be resolved, demand a quite different kind of cognition.

These problems do not only affect medicine, but also all aspects of human life, including science, economy, social and political structures, values, religious beliefs, our relation to nature, and even the arts. In short, with the old way of thinking we are coming to the end of a 500-year-old, and now outdated, materialistic and mechanical tradition. In order to anticipate the future, or even to be able to survive as a civilization, we have to cope with these difficulties, which only can be done by replacing old ways of thinking with a new kind. What would this new thinking be like?

The old way is a bottom-up mode of thinking. It starts with the perception of the material world, because we deem sensory information to be the basis for all cognition. Hence, we are transforming a physical perceptual way of relating to the outer world into an assumed parallel psychological way of understanding the same world. We thereby reduce human consciousness to be equivalent to this physical reality, or even identical with it. The result is that we see the human being, in spite of all our spiritual richness, as more or less a physical 'thing'.

This bottom-up mode of thinking tends to create problems rather than solve them. Why not proceed from the opposite direction and start with spiritual experiences? We could then proceed to explain the human mind and the physical world as the results of spiritual processes. Then we would lay a new foundation for our conception of the world and give new answers to the challenges that modern society is facing.

We would see man as embedded in a larger unity of cosmic forces instead of belonging to the disintegrated world that is the inheritance of modern science. This would then give us a better understanding of the phenomenon and significance of human life than the scientific discoveries of the last past 500 years have been able to do. It would also inspire us with hope and confidence in the future of humankind on the planet, instead of leaving us with a feeling of fear and alienation.

In this opening to a spiritual and optimistic worldview lies the task and the significance of a spiritually-based philosophy. This should explore the premises and eventual limits of such knowledge. Then humanity will feel reintegrated into the universe, as we will find that the premises for human thinking are the same as the processes that govern the spiritual world and consequently the whole cosmos. Unlike the old philosophy and science, man will not be seen as something independent and self-sufficient, but as an integral part of the processes and forces that govern the cosmos, understood both in its physical and spiritual aspects.

Such a spiritual reform of philosophy and science has been for many years my main task. At each step that I have taken in this direction, I have seen new possibilities, challenges and problems that can be resolved without being consigned to some obscure and forgotten box room in the scientific or philosophical backwaters. Because it presents us with answers to the deepest existential questions, this new philosophy is not only rational, but even more rational than traditional philosophy and science have ever been.

The present book is an important step in this direction. It explores the significance of the spiritual world for human physical and mental health, particularly the treatment of illness and life-threatening diseases.

The basic concept in the study of spiritually-caused illness is that of demons. However, today the concept of demons is so alien to most people that it needs a careful introduction that Thoresen presents us with in the book.

To understand what demons are, the first step is to acknowledge their spiritual nature. In order to do this, we have to distinguish between good and evil spirits.

Generally speaking, spirits can be divided into two classes: those that can connect with the human realm but not influence us without the human being's conscious free will and, on the other hand, those that are 'allowed' to influence humans without the victims' free will and conscious acceptance.

The former is called by Thoresen simply *spirits*. They are always benevolent to man. The others might be benevolent and even in many cases necessary for the wellbeing and development of the human being. However, they might also change into spirits that are negative to us, and even from their own nature be harmful and injurious, causing diseases, incomprehensible happenings or disasters. The author calls these spirits, *demons*.

According to Thoresen, the proper word for demons would be 'pathological structures of spiritual origin with their own life'. In other words, they are spiritual processes that have a non-benevolent effect upon humans and that can live and behave like independent spiritual beings, i.e. as individual and conscious entities.

The world of good spirits forms a hierarchy, ranging from ordinary nature spirits that are benevolent to man, to spirits of deceased people and, further on, to the hierarchies of the higher spirits (angels, archangels, etc.).

In the same way, evil or harmful spirits also parallel these categories, namely different kinds of elemental nature spirits ('sub nature spirits'), ordinary nature spirits, spirits of deceased people and the hierarchy of higher spirits, such as the ahrimanic and luciferic beings.

Elemental nature spirits and ordinary nature spirits exist in their own right, without necessarily interfering with human life, and in many cases they do so. However, many of these demons are created by the thoughts and actions of human beings, past or present. They are sustained either by a mysterious force emanating from the depths of the earth (geopathic radiation, an ahrimanic influence) or by the magnetic field of the earth (related to Lucifer). They are always involved in creation of diseases. One of the secrets of these dark forces is that they have no power of their own.

They can only feed on the fear and resistance that they initiate. The more we resist them, the more we risk that the demons suck power and strength from us if we do not fight them in the right way.

Thoresen bases his conception of the ahrimanic and luciferic spirits on the distinction made by Rudolf Steiner in a lecture in St Gallen, Switzerland on 16 November 1917. In this lecture Steiner stated that:

> Illnesses that appear spontaneously from within the human being come not through outer injuries, not from the human soul, they come from this [i.e. the ahrimanic] being. He is the creator of all illnesses that emerge spontaneously from within; he is the creator of all organic illnesses.
>
> A brother of his, who is not composed ahrimanically but luciferically, is the creator of all neurasthenic and neurotic illnesses, all the illnesses that are not really illnesses but only nervous illnesses, hysterical illnesses as they are described. Thus, medicine must become spiritual in two directions. [Steiner calls this 'organic medicine'.]

In addition to the two groups of pathological structure mentioned by Steiner, Thoresen describes a third group, known in ancient times as the azuric demons. 'In old times the luciferic demons were the most dangerous. In our present time the ahrimanic are the most dangerous, and in future times the azuric demons will be the most dangerous,' he writes.

The book deals particularly with the harm caused by the ahrimanic, luciferic and azuric forces and their helpers upon us, how they enter into us, to which part in us they adhere, which diseases they bring and how we can free ourselves from them or treat the diseases.

The three groups of pathological structures enter into human beings through the three different spiritual energy fields or auras that surround the human being:

- The ahrimanic demons relate to the growth forces or etheric aura.
- The luciferic demons relate to the feelings, the astral aura.
- The azuric demons relate to the spirit, the 'I' organization.

When these demons enter into the body, the results are always negative. Both the ahrimanic and luciferic demons can cause physical and mental illness.

Thoresen writes, 'If, for example, ahrimanic demons enter into *the physical body*, they can cause degenerative diseases (calcified articulations, arteriosclerosis, stiff joints and depressions). [. . .] If they enter into *the soul*, we become bound up with negative emotions such as greed, jealousy or anger. If they enter into *the spirit* we become confused, depressed and misled on our spiritual path.'

When luciferic spirits enter us, 'the effect is that we become self-occupied, uninterested in our fellow men, uninterested in the earth'. Further, they can 'cause us to become obsessed and manic [. . .] or become [. . .] egoistic and self-occupied. In addition, they cause painful conditions like rheumatism, chronic pain, headaches and infections. Hysteria and addictions are diagnoses that would also come under luciferic influence.' In disease, however, the ahrimanic demons are generally attached to the organ processes of the body whereas the luciferic demons are more attached to the psychic parts of the soul and are therefore connected to psychiatric conditions.

As regards the azuric demons, they 'cause us to lose our higher self, our higher "I", leaving us only with our lower "I", and as such we become too egoistic and get access to alien knowledge that can be detrimental to our human evolution'.

The demonic beings can enter man on many different levels. The further into the human being they reach, the more damage they do. The next step in understanding the demonic forces is to understand how the demonic beings create disease. Thoresen explains this in detail.

Normally, diseases happen through some wrong way of living (wrong thinking, acting, eating, drinking, feeling, clothing or other mistakes we make in our lives). This creates a deficiency in the etheric part of the organ process ('either of the heart, the pericardium, the kidneys, the lungs, the spleen or the liver', writes Thoresen), which causes forces of a subhuman nature (ahrimanic forces) to enter and develop.

However, the weakened organ process and the incarnated ahrimanic entity will not be able to perform the controlling action that a normal body process can. Therefore, another organ process will come into excess, or we might say that the excess is created as the ahrimanic demon invites in a luciferic demon. This luciferic demon usually incarnates in the astral part of the organ process controlled by the initial deficient process.

Over some time, the disease will weaken other organ processes so that a 'new' ahrimanic demon will enter. After some time, this new ahrimanic demon will invite a new luciferic demon, which then takes hold of the astral parts of the process. This weakens the etheric part and, after some time, this weakness will open up to an invasion from a third ahrimanic demon, and so on.

'When observing diseased individuals, I always see a combination of these two types of spirits, the luciferic and the ahrimanic demonic spirits,' writes Thoresen. 'The further distance in the body these two spirits are from each other, the less important the disease is. The closer they are, the more severe the disease. When they touch, we have the creation of either cancer or destructive energy.'

To put it another way, if the ahrimanic and the luciferic demons incarnate in the same organ, it often results in particular destructive diseases like cancer.

The third step in understanding the demonic forces and how they act upon the human being is to gain knowledge of the treatment of the pathological structures that they cause. Treating these structures can be done in different ways. One way is to address one of the two demons, either by weakening the luciferic demon (excessive and symptomatic treatment) or by weakening the ahrimanic demon (deficient treatment). For instance, as cancer is caused by the cooperation between the ahrimanic and luciferic demons, drugs that either strengthen the ahrimanic or the luciferic demons may help in fighting this disease. 'Today the ahrimanic demons are usually the strongest and most prolific in creating disease, so substances that strengthen the luciferic demons in a general way may be positive in cancer,' states the author.

The problem with this treatment is that the demon is simply *translocated* into another pathology, to other parts of the body or to another victim (human or animal) or might even later return to the original victim, in the meantime having grown stronger. It might also bring another demon with it.

Another method is to transform the demons. This consists in activating the 'middle' process between Ahriman and Lucifer by awakening what Thoresen calls the Christ Consciousness, or Middle Point. It is only when we do this that we can be sure that the pathological structures (the demons) are not translocated but disappear without coming back or being moved to another part of the body or another victim.

Thus, in the treatment of diseases, we are in fact dealing with three methods:

- Treating the excess, the symptoms, which is Lucifer.
- Treating the deficiency, the cause of the excess, which is Ahriman.
- Treating the Middle Point, the force which dissolves both Lucifer and Ahriman.

These three ways of treating diseases involve three different soul forces, which the author carefully separates. These forces are thinking, feeling and will. They can be used on their own or in combination.

Thinking is the initial form of soul force used in the treatment, in the initial stage of the diagnosis of any patient, both animal and man. We must ask ourselves about the disease, make our observations and think through how we will perform the whole operation. (Is surgery needed, do we need any medications? and so on.)

After this initial stage, we have to proceed into separating the three soul forces. Quoting Steiner, Thoresen explains that the entanglement of thinking, feeling and will, which are three cosmic and divine forces originating in the spiritual world and not within ourselves, is the main reason why we are anchored in the physical world. When man, consisting of body, soul and spirit, is incarnated in the physical world, our thinking, feeling and will are interwoven and bound together.

Thoresen writes:

> The real content, function, power and origin of the three soul forces are hidden from us, as they overshadow each other. We are led to believe that thinking, feeling and will are just faculties developed or produced by ourselves, and forever interdependent. [...] It is as if we would believe that the colours are within the eye, created by ourselves, and that the sounds are within the ear, created by the brain. It is the same with thinking, feeling and will.

However, the real force of thinking, feeling and will is not to the same extent hidden from us:

- The least hidden force is *thinking*.
- The half-conscious and half-hidden force is *feeling*.
- The strongest but most hidden force is *will*.

In order to be aware of their cosmic origin, and the immense forces that are hidden within thinking, feeling and will, we have to separate them from each other, and then they can perform wonders. The reason for this is that in these three forces we 'become part of the cosmos [...] part of the Gods, part of the spiritual world'.

The separation of thinking, feeling and will can be achieved through knowing their secrets, but also through meditation and concentration. According to the author, this act of separation is of crucial importance to the treatment process, as they constitute three different ways of relating to the diseases. In order to treat the excesses (Lucifer), we use thinking ('our head, the white light and the rhythms of the head'). To treat the deficiency, we activate our will ('our digestion and earthy, rhythmic energy'). In order to treat both by dissolving them, we should activate or use only our feeling ('that is our love, our heart, our sunlight, our inner Christ'). Thoresen writes:

We use the force of will to conquer the dominion of Ahriman. We use the thinking force to conquer the dominion of Lucifer. From the feeling and the heart forces we feel reverence for the balancing and dissolving presence of the Christ, of his love. Then a lasting healing may occur, and also no translocation of the disease.

The central concept in the treatment of diseases is the Christ Principle or the Middle Point. However, today it is equally difficult to talk about Christ Consciousness as it is to talk about the existence of demons. Both in alternative circles and in the general population, the name of Christ is devalued and scorned. The disdain for the Light of Christ is also a result of how the church has acted over the centuries, often in a very contrary way to what Jesus taught.

The Christ Principle is about staying in the middle, between the excess and the deficiency, between Lucifer and Ahriman. Christ, even in his last minutes inside the human body of Jesus, hung in the middle between two robbers: one representing the luciferic (the one that was saved), and the other the ahrimanic sins (the one that was not saved).

The challenge for the practitioner is to find the middle process in the human being ('The luciferic structures are almost always proximal or cranial, whereas the ahrimanic structures are almost always distal or caudal. The Middle Point is a little closer to the excess,' Thoresen writes.) We must then use our Christ Consciousness, our love and understanding, to treat the middle process between the luciferic and ahrimanic structures. Within the Christ Consciousness, we will be experiencing cosmic, divine love and when we are doing so, we will not only be transforming the demons, but we will also free them so that they are 'healed'. It is important to remember here that divine love is a love that, strictly speaking, is 'all love'. It does not yield to the attraction of its object. It is not aiming at a particular being. It shoots beyond each being and only reaches the universe by passing through the whole universe.

'Only Christ and the Christ Consciousness have the power to free demons,' writes Thoresen. To the author of this Foreword, this statement expresses a profound acknowledgement of the fundamental cosmic power that sustains the world. As previously mentioned, it has almost been totally forgotten about today.

Therefore, in order to truly understand what demons are, a fourth and last step is necessary. This step consists in the awareness of the greater macrocosmic spiritual processes to which these microcosmic pathological processes belong. In fact, they are part of a greater battle between good and evil forces in the universe.

Originally, demons belonged to the angelic realms, where they were created by earlier actions of even higher beings, possibly when the angels were at their 'human' stage. These demons (for example Lucifer) are angels left behind from previous periods of cosmic development.

Before then, eons ago, Ahriman had already broken away from the angelic realm. He descended to the earth, where he found a home in the deep layers of the planet. Therefore, the influences of Ahriman have to do with powers of a much lower nature than the influences of Lucifer. Lucifer's influences can never become as evil as the influences of Ahriman and of those beings that are connected with the ahrimanic spirits.

How did the luciferic and ahrimanic forces enter into man? When man became an embodied being (i.e. when the higher 'I' descended from the spiritual world and became ensnared by desires and cravings under the influence of Lucifer, and then, caught by Ahriman's influence, became immersed in the earthly, physical world of lies, error and illusion) something was lost. What was lost was man's direct connection to the cosmos, the understanding of the spiritual world and how it operates. To put it in another way, man lost the connection to his spiritual 'I'.

Thanks to the void that was created in the human body when man became embodied in the physical world, the luciferic and ahrimanic forces had a possibility to enter. They even *had* to do so because these forces have no bodies of their own. By incorporating into the humans, not only do they try to conquer the Earth and take possession of human beings, they also try to take over the rulership of both the material and the spiritual world. The first step is to take control over human beings. This strengthens them in the higher, spiritual battle.

The battle will be fought through our *thinking*, our *feeling* and our *will*. 'If these three abilities of the human soul are taken over by the adversaries, we are lost for eternity as a human race,' writes Thoresen. 'Therefore, the time for speaking about demons is ripe; in fact, the time is overripe.'

The knowledge of the adversaries, the soul forces and the Christ are of crucial importance today. Such knowledge will work as a healing impulse in humanity, opening the way for Christ, the only force that can counteract the power of the adversaries, Ahriman, Lucifer and their legions of helping demons. These are all working in the Earth, in our bodies, our souls and our spirits, causing disease, materialism, atheism and immorality, but through Christ they will then be conquered and finally released.

At the same time, we must understand that it is important to respect demons. They also have their own life and destiny, as Thoresen emphasizes:

- Demons *want* to be transformed into the light.
- Demons are trapped in the grip of the adversaries and *want* to become free.
- When we see, hear or sense demons, we need to understand that the mere sensing of the demons gives us some power over them.
- Christ and Christ Consciousness have the power to free demons.

In this insight lies the deep significance of the Mystery of Golgotha and Christ.

The author writes:

> In my opinion it must be emphasized that the Christ individuality, the cosmic force that incarnated in Jesus of Nazareth, is the only force that can counteract the destructive force emanated by the ahrimanic and luciferic demons. [...] In my knowledge of Tantrism, Hinduism, Buddhism or any other spiritual movement, I have not found a deeper understanding of this unique force.

★

Thoresen's book is an introduction to the spiritual world. As such, it presents a comprehensive study of the spiritual world's significance and importance to medicine. Though spiritual medicine is an old concept, the book, as far as I know, is the first one to present a spiritual medicine in the context of modern civilization and the diseases connected with it. This gives the book an insight into the errors and mistaken steps that modern society has taken and is still taking.

Of most importance is the insistence on the power of Christ and his mission. In the book, Christ is not only treated as the incarnated historical person of Jesus, but as the fundamental principle of the forces that lie at the root of the evolution of the universe. Today we have forgotten all about demons and even about Christ. Both concepts have become anachronisms from olden times. That they are not anachronisms is illustrated in the discussions and examples given in this book.

The book is highly recommended to everyone who wants a comprehensive understanding of the higher processes that man is part of and an explanation as to why it is so important that we are aware of these processes. Thanks to this knowledge, we can better understand the human condition today.

Hans Kolstad
Dethsgård, Læsø (Denmark), August 2016

Preface

Just as Newton asked himself *why* the apple fell to the ground and thus started a completely new world of understanding, we must also ask ourselves about the real cause of the following observations.

Within both acupuncture and homeopathy, *Hering's law* describes how diseases leave the body. For instance, a migraine, which physically may be caused by a pulsating artery upon a local nerve, travels from the head and all along the body, and leaves through the feet. It may be that a disease located deep within the body then slowly travels more and more to the periphery and leaves through the skin. All therapists have seen this. We have also seen how diseases, or the causes of diseases in humans, may be transferred to an animal, indeed to a whole herd of sheep. A disease in the parents may go over to the children and to an animal. I have experienced that a severe disease in a patient may jump over to me, and that I immediately get a strong migraine. In addition, we all have seen how a disease develops in time, and when we treat the disease correctly, this development may be reversed; it goes back in time, so to speak.

What is the reality behind these observations? How can they be explained? What, actually, is travelling around? What is it that is jumping from one person to another? These are questions that we *must* ask ourselves, both to understand and to be able to treat a disease.

The answer, in my humble opinion, is that the disease is the result of the presence of a noxious or pathological structure, a structure that may travel, jump, dislocate, develop itself, and also change to a former state of development. This pathological structure behaves like an entity. There are two sorts of such pathological beings (yin and yang).

When we treat, whether with homeopathy, acupuncture or herbs, there are two possible outcomes from a seemingly successful treatment: either the pathological structure is dissolved or it is translocated. If we treat the symptoms (which I will call the *excess*), even if we treat the cause (which I will call the *deficiency*), the pathological structure is usually just translocated. We think then that the disease is healed, but it is just hidden or moved.

For a long time, I have observed this happen for me and for my colleagues (I would say that it happens in 90% of all alternative treatments), and the most important question for me in the last years has been how to truly dissolve the disease. This translocation gives a point of departure for the understanding of the observed connection between all living entities.

There is a strong energetic connection between all levels of creation: we are all connected energetically through the existence of the elementals—both the spirits and the demons, in the following ways:

- Between Cosmos and Earth. Which is why disease changes with changing external situations and thus gives rise to all the diagnostic systems based upon this.
- Between Earth and all living creatures, which explains the same as the above, together with 'geopathy'.
- Between all living creatures. Which is the foundation for my way of doing pulse diagnosis, anthroposophical medicine and osteopathy.
- Between all parts within a living entity. Which is an explanation for why ECIWO-systems* work, in fact a basis for the complete holistic approach in medicine.

The old shamans healed in the consciousness of nature: they felt connected to the forces and gods of nature, and they felt this bond between all creatures.

As we will see in this book, this total connection to creation leaves us also vulnerable to invasion by elemental beings. The only way to keep safe and sound is to strengthen the spirit, our own self-consciousness. That is why the most important task of future spirituality is to strengthen the 'I' or Ego-function of man. That is, the cosmic and divine Ego-function, not the egoistic 'I'.

*

Moses was the first person to call God, 'I am'. Jesus told the people that he was a messenger from 'I am': he even called himself 'the I am'. The truth is to be found within you.

Søren Kierkegaard was the first philosopher who, in 1851, proclaimed that the subjective self was the truth and that the general consensus was the untruth. The Norwegian author and philosopher J.S. Welhaven and the Danish philosopher F.C. Sibbern inspired Søren Kierkegaard.

Welhaven expressed himself as follow: 'Hegelians do not study

---

*ECIWO is an acronym that means *Embryo Containing Information of the Whole Organism*. It indicates that all cells and parts of the body contain information of the whole body. All these systems communicate with each other and with the whole organism. Because of this, all microsystems (ECIWO-systems) may be used in therapy and in diagnosis. There are different levels of ECIWO-systems. The lowest or primary level is the DNA-molecule as such. This molecule contains information about the whole organism and can give rise to all the cells in the organism. The next level is the cell, then the organ, the organ-system and then the whole organism as such.

philosophy existentially.' In other words, Hegel did not comprehend it as a living experience (or a life-experience) in the subject: in this respect, truth cannot be digitalized, formalized, stored on a shelf or sold over the counter. Kierkegaard turned against Hegel, who died in 1831, when Kierkegaard was 18 years old.

In the middle of the 1900s, existentialism spread in Europe, and the most important proponents were Gabriel Marcel, Karl Jaspers, Martin Heidegger and Jean Paul Sartre.

Rudolf Steiner said that, 'only in thinking the will can you find the truth and the forces available for healing'.

Margit Engel expresses likewise: 'Healing is only possible if you activate your courage.' And by 'courage' she meant 'will–intention–consciousness'.

Modern physics also proclaims that consciousness is necessary to explain the behaviour of quanta, and it is now considered as a part of quantum physics.

In modern times, philosophers like Tomas Nagel proclaimed that consciousness is necessary to comprehend reality, and indeed a part of reality which science so far has not integrated in its (mostly) materialistic worldview.

Susan Blackmore and Paul Churchland, on the other side, declare consciousness as a grand illusion. They think (!) that consciousness does not truly exist, other than as an 'illusion of being conscious'.

The consciousness that I will here try to explain or describe in this book is of great importance when diagnosing and treating, otherwise we may even harm our patients. This consciousness reveals the hidden relationships between all living beings, both human and animal, and how therapists may cause harm to those connected with patients without realizing it.

★

Throughout my life, my professional life in particular, I have been able to observe diseases both through pulse diagnosis and by seeing the distorted and pathological energetic structures directly with the help of an elevated sensitivity. I have then observed that when the disease has been treated, whether through acupuncture, chiropractic, osteopathy, homeopathy or herbal medicine, the pathological structure has merely been relocated to another place in the body, or into another entity, animal or human. Sometimes the patho-structure just takes a little round trip, and then returns to its original place. We then say that the disease has reappeared.

I want to shed a conscious light on the fact that, when treated, diseases caused by energetic and self-containing structures may influence or 'attack' other beings, change, or just come back. This description of diseases sounds a lot like descriptions of real and living entities.

There are many stories and insights from olden times and old religions, where disease and ailments were regarded as separate and individualized entities, or energetically self-conscious structures, described as elementals, spirits, demons or devas. Many of us have experienced that if we are too open in the moment of acupuncture treatment, the energetic patho- logical structure may jump over, attack us and inflict us with the disease itself. We have also seen that such pathological structures may inflict, influence or create disease in creatures connected to the patient.

We are all interwoven in an enormous web of energy, a web that connects all living entities in the world, maybe the whole cosmos. This web is to be seen just on the other side of the threshold of the spiritual world. It is called by many names, such as the *akashic record*, *karma* or *the matrix*. This web is made of energy, but not just lifeless and aimless energy. It is made up of elementals: living etheric beings, created by our minds, our thoughts and our actions. This web is also part of our diseases and is influenced when we treat energetically.

In olden times, and still we may see this phenomenon today, the doors to temples of small communities were bordered by the pictures or sculptures of ugly-looking demons. This was to scare the real demons or negative spirits away, to scare diseases away.

There is a moving story about Jesus, told by Rudolf Steiner in his lecture cycle *The Fifth Gospel*:

> When in his 20s, he visited one of the Essene communities. He realized that the sculptures around the door scared or drove the evil spirits away, but then a very important question arose in his mind; to where were the spirits driven? Then he understood that it was no solution just to drive the bad spirits away to other people, to save somebody at the cost of creating disease in others. This question and realization opened his mind to be the receiver of the Christ, the redeemer of all.

Rudolf Steiner described the same phenomenon in his lectures entitled *Introducing Anthroposophical Medicine*:

> The concept of infection, however, is none the less valid here. For any highly tuberculous individual affects his fellow beings and if any person is exposed to the sphere in which the tuberculous patient lives, then it may happen that the effect turns again into a cause. I have often tried to illustrate the relationship between primary causes of a disease and infection in the following analogy: Suppose that I meet a friend of

mine, whose relations with other people do not in general touch me. He is sad and has reason to be so, for he has lost one of his friends by death. I have no direct relationship with this friend who has died, but I become sad with him at his sad news. His sadness is, so to speak, first hand and direct; mine arises indirectly, communicated through him. Nevertheless, the fact remains that the mutual relationship between my friend and me provides the pre-condition for this 'infection'.*

He continues in another lecture:

The method referred to would consist in making every possible effort to make the Ritter therapy universally accepted. In face of successes of this treatment, you forget that you work as individual physicians. Possibly individuals among you may be aware of the struggle you have to wage against the majority of other doctors, and you may be aware that the moment you make Ritter's treatment into an accepted university institution, you would cease to be a minority in opposition, and that treatment would then be practised by many others—I will not go so far as to say by all. You would then find the number of your successful cures appreciably diminished. So strangely do things befall in real life; they are often quite different from what we have imagined. As individual medical men you have the greatest interest in healing the individual patient, and modern materialistic medicine has even, one might say, sought in this way a legal justification for its aim of healing the individual, but this justification really consists in the claim that there are no diseases; there are only sick, diseased people! Now, this justification would be valid if patients were really so isolated regarding their sickness, as appears to be the case today. But in actual fact, individual patients are not so isolated. The fact that certain dispositions of disease spread over a wide region, as was mentioned yesterday by Dr E., is of great importance. After curing one case, you can never be sure of the number of other individuals to whom you have brought the disease. A single case of a disease is not viewed as part of a general process, and therefore, taken one by one, the individual result may be most striking.†

This communication is not random or by chance. As a key fits a lock, it is possible to work therapeutically *only with similar etheric forces*; those with a structural congruence or empathy, a similar feeling, or those in direct communication.

We often see that etheric weaknesses in the owner manifest in the

---

*Lecture of 22 March, 1920, Dornach.
†Lecture of 24 March, 1920, Dornach.

animal attached to him or her. This is easy to see in regards to temperament shared by the dog owner and the dog, but this communication applies to all animals—cows, horses, sheep, pigs and their keepers. A nervous, irritable owner often has nervous, irritable animals.

As we have seen above, there is a close etheric connection between all living beings. This is good concerning health and treatment, but equally hazardous concerning the transfer of diseases between them.

All diseases may be viewed as pathological information expressed in the etheric body, in the energetic structure of any living being. All treatments are directed to change the pathology into a beneficial energetic structure and the restoration of health. However, this is not always so easy to perform. Actually, it is quite difficult.

According to my observations, most treatments show an inability to dissolve or transform the pathological structures, and the disease may then choose several other possibilities. It may 'sort of' disappear for a short while, as if it went underground, and then reappear. It may change and then appear in another form, with changed symptomatology. It may appear in another tissue or organ and there cause a problem after a certain amount of time, which may be years. A treatment of a cough may thus reappear after three years as a breast cancer. It may travel over to another entity, human or animal. As previously stated, an etheric pathological structure will always influence all the living creatures in the surroundings of the diseased, but in treatment the channels to the surroundings are 'sort of' opened, so that this influence goes much faster and stronger.

Different symptoms in the patient—the seeming disappearance of the symptoms, the appearance of different diseases after some time and several unexplained diseases in other living creatures in the patient's surroundings—may be the result, and these are very difficult to recognize.

How do we relate to this somewhat discouraging information? A possible solution was given to me during a consultation with the author and lecturer Judith von Halle, in the summer of 2013 in Dornach. She told me that the only way to hinder any pathological energy structure or information from proceeding along its karmic paths, in the process inflicting also the karmic connections of the diseased entity, was to treat with the Christ Consciousness.

To do so it is also important to meet, in treating the disease, the cause of the disease in its karmic consequences, described by Rudolf Steiner as 'meeting the three animals of the abyss'. These three animals shine out their dirty and twisted light: blue, red and yellow, the distorted thinking, feeling and will.

It is then up to the therapist—his insight, knowledge and love.

Introduction

On waking up early one morning in February 2016, one single thought was in my mind: 'I have to write a book on demons. This is of utmost importance for our present culture.'

In the process of writing this book, I asked several friends what they thought of the idea of writing on such a theme. Their answers were almost all the same: 'The concept of demons is so alien today for most people that you will have to write a long introduction, opening your readers to the possibility that spiritual beings actually exist. Then you must carefully introduce the concept of both good spirits and evil spirits.'

I understood that the book I was writing was too direct regarding the main subject, and that it would probably only interest my anthroposophical friends, who already accept the existence of a spiritual world. That is why I have included here what is in effect a 'demonology for beginners'. The first part of this Introduction will lead the reader into the concepts of demonology as I have developed and understood them over the course my life.

As this 'science of demonology' is not actually scientific at all, and few sources are available, this Introduction has to be quite personal. Therefore, I will start at the beginning and tell you why and how I came to believe and even *see* the spiritual beings described here.

★

Throughout my whole life, I have had a tendency to be able to excarnate (go with my soul out of the body, or to put it another way, divide my thinking, feeling and will—this will be explained later in great detail). This ability may have been because of what I believed was epilepsy, or it may have been that what I thought were epileptic symptoms appeared because of the above-mentioned separation of soul faculties obtained through karma and previous earth lives.

Therefore, from my early youth I regularly experienced 'strange' phenomena, which I did not acknowledge as spiritual, as at that time and up to the age of 17 I defined myself as an atheist.

I was six years old the first time I experienced something paranormal (apart from the regular going-out-of-the-body connected to the epileptic symptoms I suffered). I have repeated this experience several times, and it has always turned out to be correct. Early one morning the telephone rang, and I was sure that somebody had died, someone close to me. My first thoughts were of my dad. My mother took the telephone and started to cry. She told me that my granddad was dead. I said, 'Oh good,' (meaning that it was good that my father was not dead). My mother never asked me why I had said what I did. Today I know that a death has occurred even before the telephone rings.

From quite early on in life I could *see* through hands—I could see what was inside a fisted hand. I experienced this seeing as completely physical, but I understand now that it must have been spiritual. I used this, for what it was worth, when my father and I played chess. I did not like to start, so the first hundred times we played I always chose the black pawn inside my father's fisted hand. My father wondered why I always got the black pawn, but for me it was so obvious that I never even mentioned or explained it to him. It was not until I reached the age of 21 that I was told by an anthroposophical doctor, 'You know that it is not normal to be able to see through hands?'

During my teenage years nothing unusual happened, except that later I learned that girls were afraid of me because they felt that I could 'see through them'. This was told to me years later when one of the girls came to me as a patient.

When I was 21, the paranormal experiences started again. In the summer of 1973, I had the most interesting experience. I was working as a shepherd in the mountains of Norway, in Kvam, Gudbrandsdalen. Suddenly, one evening, in the light Norwegian summer night, a stone jumped over the trail I was following, and then, for three days, I could speak (as a dialogue) with the trees. And speak with them I did, something that gave me much of the material to my book, *Poppel—Poplar— Pappel*.

My first encounter with *evil* was one evening some years later, in 1978, as I went home from the veterinary high school. It was winter and the streets were dead. I turned a corner and entered a new block. From the other side of the street, coming straight towards me, was another human being—or at least so I thought. As we both walked closer and closer I heard drums in the air which became louder and louder. When I was only one metre away, just before passing this other entity, the sound of the drums reverberating in the air was very strong. As we passed I gazed into 'his' face, which was covered by a hood, but to my horror there was no face there. I was terrified, but walked on, and as I walked away from this entity, the drums weakened more and more, until they finally died out.

After I graduated as a veterinarian and moved to Northern Norway, the encounters with evil and death became more frequent. In 1980, when

I was a veterinarian in Bodø, Northern Norway, my wife at that time had a visit from a friend. When I came into the room, I *saw* a 'structure', half out of the friend's left skull and half still within the head. It was like a spiral or a curled snake. She told me that she was suffering a painful migraine. I went towards this woman and took hold of the energetic 'structure' with my hand. I pulled it halfway out, and the woman said that the pain diminished. Then I let go of the 'structure', and it slipped immediately back into her head. 'Ow,' she said, 'now the pain has come back!' Again, I grabbed hold of the 'structure' and pulled it all the way out. The migraine totally disappeared. I was now very careful with what I did to the 'structure' that I held in my hand. I went to the open window and threw it out. It did not return.

In the following years, in fact until the present, I have asked myself repeatedly, 'What was that structure, from where had it come and where did it go after I threw it out of the window? Did it come back?' These questions became very important for me. The answers to them are essential for understanding the existence of demons and their part in disease.

Although I was working in Northern Norway, I occasionally had to travel to Oslo, where by chance I met the great and famous doctor, Georg Bentze. He later became my teacher in acupuncture. One day at his office, a corona suddenly appeared around his head, emitting a strong light and almost blinding me. In this light there was a date, and I knew intuitively that this was the date of his death. It was eleven months in the future. He died exactly on that day.

This experience brought several new questions to my mind.

- Is our day of death destined?
- Is destiny real?
- What is karma?

One time when I was in a barn treating a cow with milk fever (hypocalcemia), the cow suddenly died, even though I had given an appropriate treatment. Fourteen days later I was in the same barn, this time with a new cow also suffering with milk fever, and again it died under my hands and treatment. After the third cow had died, again 14 days later, I questioned the farmer, 'Why are all your cows dying?' He told me that they had been 'ganned' by a neighbour, who was of Sami origin, and that all his cows would die. Whether or not this was a fact, I do not know. Anyhow, I then performed a ritual isolating the whole barn from evil. After that, no more cows died.

Often when I treated diseases with homeopathy or acupuncture, which I then used more and more in my practice on animals and their owners, the symptoms moved around in the body. Over three to four months of repeated treatment, a migraine could move down into the hand and end up as a pain in the little finger. As a medically-trained person, I knew that migraine is caused by a pulsating artery that affects a nerve in the head, so this moving around appeared quite strange to me, quite inexplicable.

I then had to pose the very important question to myself: 'What is it that travels from the brain into the little finger and remains there?'

Then I began to see and understand more and more what the reality was behind the 'travelling structures' of diseases:

- They are structures that have their own life that can travel in the body from top to bottom.
- They can also jump over to another person, or to an animal.
- They are structures that are alive. Ordinary treatment with physiotherapy, osteopathy, acupuncture, painkillers and other allopathic medicines only moves these structures to other places in the body or to other individuals.

In my practice, as well as in the practices of all my colleagues, I became painfully aware that we all merely translocated the noxious structure, the symptoms, and for this we received money!

I felt more and more like a fraud. In 2005, I knew I had to change something so that my treatments would become 'true'. I became progressively aware that these structures, these symptoms, could not be fought—they had to be transformed. The question is, how can we transform something that is a living entity? I then started to treat these noxious structures in my work with acupuncture as if they really were living entities. I did not fight them anymore. I simply treated the Middle Point, also called the Christ Consciousness point, allowing them to transform. I have demonstrated this technique several times for colleagues and students and the results have been very good.

At a seminar in Germany I treated a horse from the Middle Point with Christ Consciousness. After giving the treatment, 'something' came out of the horse, and this 'something' swirled around inside the circle of observing students. They should not have been standing in a circle, as that captured the 'something'. Then it disappeared into thin air. One of the students happened to attract a part of this 'something' that was released. She went home after the seminar and became sick. Thanks to her therapist, who was able to quickly diagnose this 'partial pathological structure' and release it, she got away without serious damage. The 'something' was stuck in her heart, where it tried to make its new home.

So, what is this 'something'? As we will see throughout this book, this 'something' lives and behaves as an individual and conscious entity and is no less than a *demon*.

The name 'demon' calls forth disbelief in many readers. I could have described the entities as pathological or noxious structures with qualities of either Yin or Yang and with their own life, but this would not have been honest. I prefer to call them by their old name, demons.

- The 'pathological or noxious structure of Yin quality with its own life' I call an ahrimanic demon.
- The 'pathological or noxious structure of Yang quality with its own life' I call a luciferic demon.

Human thoughts and misdeeds, past or present, create these demons. Geopathic radiation, a mysterious force emanating from the depths of the earth, sustains the demons, which always trigger disease if they attach to a human or animal.

This book explains the role of demons in disease and how conscious invocation of Christ, and the help of the good forces of Christ's realm, can help affected people and animals.

★

I recently had a discussion about the reality of demons with a Protestant priest working in the Norwegian church. 'Does the church believe in the existence of demons?', was my question. He became irritated and answered that he would not talk about this. 'We avoid this subject within the church,' was his answer.

If we look in the Gospels, there are numerous stories about demons, but the church refuses to see this. Jesus Christ and his disciples healed many people by driving away demons. A tenth of the Gospels are about this phenomenon. Still, it remains a taboo within the church. This is sad, but unfortunately very understandable.

Our Western culture, with its rational and materialistic viewpoint, finds the concept of non-material and invisible beings utterly irrational. The people who started the Icelandic Elf School (Bryndís Pétursdóttir) or the Norwegian Angel School (Princess Märtha Louise) are ridiculed by the 'enlightened' population and are considered by most people to be crazy. We 'normal people' do not believe in a spiritual world, inhabited by spiritual beings.

This disbelief in a spiritual world is very negative for the development of our culture and society. We have totally lost the reverence for both ourselves and for other beings, and no longer consider plants, trees or animals as spiritual beings. Not even human beings are considered spiritual beings by science. If we could consider ourselves, as well as the rest of creation, as 'beings of spirit', then we would have a much deeper respect for all living creations. Perhaps then we would also stop damaging, killing and destroying the world as we do today. Even agriculture, animal farming, fishing and hunting would obtain a new understanding.

This worldview is almost out of reach today. The majority of people consider the world as a means to satisfy themselves, and endless greed is all we see. The only possible salvation I can envisage is that we begin to understand that we are sharing this earth with a multitude of both seen and unseen spiritual beings.

We can see with our material eyes the plants and the animals, the trees and the flowers, the insects and the wind, the water and the smoke, the whole visible totality of the good earth. In addition to all the beings that we can see physically, however, we are surrounded by a huge variety of spiritual beings that are not visible to the material eye. We can see or sense these spiritual beings (good and evil) only by our sixth sense—our 'third eye' or our 'spiritual heart eye'.

Firstly, there are elemental beings inhabiting the Water, Air, Earth and Fire. They are everywhere and in the entirety of nature. They are the spiritual basis of all that we see around us.

Then we have the 'group souls' of the plants, the 'plant souls'. They are often described as 'flower fairies'. Every single flower has its fairy. Likewise, every single tree has its own spirit.

Animals also have their 'fairies', although this word may not so easily be used in connection with animals, as the elemental beings connected with them may often look ugly and not at all fairy-like.

Crystals in nature also have spirits connected to them, hovering over them.

Then, there are myriads of spirits connected to the so-called 'earth radiation', the energetic grid of the Earth (much more on this later). They are created by human thoughts, by human feelings and by human actions. They are closely connected to what is known as human karma. These spirits are bound to the people that created them as well as to the places where they were created.

The variety of these spiritual beings is huge. In Sweden, diviners have been able to categorize more than one hundred kinds of entities. Some are connected to greed, some to hate, some to murder, some to theft, and so on. The ones connected to lies are the most common.

The main groups of spirits and demons in my worldview

Sub-Nature Spirits:
The elemental realm (consisting of the totality of the Earth and cosmos)

various beings (spirits, which I am not personally able to classify)
demonic beings.

The elemental realm (what the elements consist of in their foundation)

various beings (spirits)
demonic beings.

The elemental realm (entities that we usually see in nature)

various beings (spirits):
   gnomes
   sylphs
   undines
   salamanders
demonic beings (demons):
   gnomes
   sylphs
   undines
   salamanders.

Ordinary Nature Spirits:

crystal spirits (living in rocks)
   in 'ordinary' crystals = spirits
   in toxic crystals = (resemble demonic beings)
plant spirits (living in plants)
   in 'ordinary' plants[*]
   in poisonous plants (resemble demonic beings)
   animal spirits (animal group souls—relates to astral spirits and can be
   both demonic and spiritual).

Human Spirits: human souls between death and a new (re)birth

Nine Hierarchies of Angels:

9th hierarchy

---

[*] See Findhorn, an eco-village in Scotland, where the founders claimed to speak with the plant spirits.

Angels
demons of the rank of Angels
8th hierarchy
Archangels
demons of the rank of Archangels
7th hierarchy
Archai
demons of the rank of Archai
6th hierarchy—Exusiai
5th hierarchy—Dynamis
4th hierarchy—Kyriotetes
3rd hierarchy—Thrones
2nd hierarchy—Cherubim
1st hierarchy—Seraphim

(To my knowledge, there are no demons equal to the ranks of angels of the 1st to 6th hierarchies.)

Here we must touch upon a fundamental issue: the 'good' spirits, such as angels, plant spirits, animal spirits and crystal spirits, are beneficial to human growth and evolvement because they respect our development as human beings. They do not enter us with force and nor do they intrude upon us without our permission; rather, they respect our free will.

Demonic entities are different, however. They are not beneficial to our spiritual development as conscious 'I' beings. They do not give us free choice; rather, they seek to impose their will upon us.

Teachings regarding evil spirits are central to all religions, shamanistic or spiritual systems. As we will see, evil spirits can cause damage and bring about diseases in addition to compromising our freedom.

We find teachings about these evil spirits in all spiritual systems throughout the world. For example, just think of the gargoyles, monsters, demons and maras depicted on most temples and churches.

★

Directly attached to humans themselves (although not via the earth's radiation), we find spirits of a higher rank than the spirits of 'earth radiation/karma'. They are mostly ahrimanic or luciferic elementals. These elementals are necessary for our wellbeing and development. They may transform, by a lesser or greater degree, into demonic beings, depending on our way of life or how sick or healthy we are. In disease, these elementals may be called ahrimanic demons (see later) and are attached to the organic processes of the body. Luciferic demons are more attached to the psychic parts of the soul and are connected to psychiatric conditions.

When observing diseased individuals, my 'spiritual eyes' always see a combination of these two types of spirits: the luciferic and the ahrimanic demonic spirits. The further these two spirits are from each other in the body, the less important the disease is. The closer they are together, the more severe the disease. When they touch or are superimposed, their destructive energy is most severe. Unless they can be separated and dissolved, luciferic and ahrimanic demons that touch each other in the body always cause cancer.

A special spirit called the Death Spirit lingers behind every human. The distance between the physical body and the Death Spirit indicates the length of remaining life in the physical realm.

The ahrimanic entity called the 'doppelgänger' or 'double' is of special importance. Oscar Wilde described this entity in his book, *The Picture of Dorian Grey*. Dostoyevsky also described it in his book, *The Double*.

Rudolf Steiner described the doppelgänger as the most important ahrimanic entity or spirit connected to our body. It is responsible for our wellbeing and our disease. If we live a destructive life, the ahrimanic doppelgänger becomes more and more demonic in character.

Rudolf Steiner

Rudolf Joseph Lorenz Steiner (1861–1925) was an Austrian philosopher, author, social reformer, architect and esotericist. Steiner gained initial recognition at the end of the nineteenth century as a literary critic and published philosophical works including *The Philosophy of Freedom*. At the beginning of the twentieth century, he founded an esoteric spiritual movement, anthroposophy, with roots in German idealist philosophy and theosophy. Other influences include Goethean science and Rosicrucianism. In the first, more philosophically oriented phase of this movement, Steiner attempted to find a synthesis between science and spirituality. His philosophical work from these years, which he termed spiritual science, sought to apply the clarity of thinking characteristic of western philosophy to spiritual questions differentiating this approach from what he considered vague approaches to mysticism. In the second phase, beginning around 1907, he began working collaboratively in a variety of artistic media, including drama, the movement arts (developing a new artistic form, eurythmy) and architecture, culminating in the building of the Goetheanum, a cultural centre to house all the activities of anthroposophy. In the third phase of his work, beginning after World War I, Steiner worked to establish various practical endeavours, including Waldorf education, bio-dynamic agriculture and anthroposophical medicine.

Steiner advocated a form of ethical individualism, to which he later brought a more explicitly spiritual approach. He based his epistemology on Johann Wolfgang von Goethe's worldview, in which 'thinking ... is no more and no less an organ of perception than the eye or ear. Just as the eye perceives colours and the ear sounds, so thinking perceives ideas.' A consistent thread that runs from his earliest philosophical phase through his later spiritual orientation is the goal of demonstrating that there are no essential limits to human knowledge. In 1899, Steiner experienced what he described as a life-transforming inner encounter with the being of Christ. Previously he had little or no relation to Christianity in any form. Then and thereafter, his relationship to Christianity remained entirely founded upon personal experience and was thus both non-denominational and strikingly different from conventional religious forms. Steiner was then 38 years of age, and the experience of meeting the Christ occurred after a tremendous inner struggle. To use Steiner's own words, the 'experience culminated in my standing in the spiritual presence of the Mystery of Golgotha in a most profound and solemn festival of knowledge'.

In a lecture held in St Gallen, Switzerland, on 16 November 1917, Rudolf Steiner said,

This doppelgänger about which I have spoken is nothing more or less than the creator of all physical illnesses that emerge spontaneously from within, and to know him fully is organic medicine. Illnesses that appear spontaneously from within the human being come, not through outer injuries, not from the human soul: they come from this being. He is the creator of all illnesses that emerge spontaneously from within; he is the creator of all organic illnesses. A brother of his, who is not composed ahrimanically but luciferically, is the creator of all neurasthenic and neurotic illnesses, all the illnesses that are not really illnesses but only nervous illnesses, 'hysterical illnesses' as they are described. Thus, medicine must become spiritual in two directions. The demand for this is shown by the intrusion of views such as those of psychoanalysis and the like, where one keeps house with spiritual entities, as it were, but with inadequate means of knowledge, so that one can do nothing at all with the phenomena that will intrude more and more into human life. For certain things need to happen, things that may even be harmful in a certain direction, because the human being must be exposed to what is harmful in order to overcome it and thereby gain strength.

In Chapter Two we will discuss both Steiner and the doppelgänger in more depth.

★

The most fierce-looking demons I have ever seen are closely attached to the altars in Protestant churches. They are always situated on the left side of the altar, as seen from the congregation. The worst demon I saw was lurking behind the altar of a church in Iceland.

The situation is somewhat different in Roman Catholic churches. The demons around the altar are smaller. They manifest as a white light, floating circa 20 metres above the floor. During the Catholic ritual of the Mass, this light descends on the congregation and streams around. I have never seen this phenomenon during a Protestant Eucharist or service.

The spirit/soul of dead people may also hover over living humans, waiting to enter whilst their alcoholic host is drinking alcohol, their drug-user host is taking drugs or sex-addict host is having sex. They are like parasites and may cause prominent changes in personality and create severe cravings.

Luckily, there are also good spirits: many of the nature spirits are benevolent and many of the spirits of deceased people are good. The hierarchies of higher spirits are also good to us. The angels, the archangels, and so on, help us.

However, apart from the ahrimanic and luciferic spirits and their helpers, there is another category of adversaries called the *azuric* spirits, which are not beneficial to the human being.

In this book, unless prefixed by a negative term, i.e., 'evil' or 'malevolent' etc., the term 'spirits' *always* denotes benevolent entities. The term 'demons' *always* denotes malevolent or noxious entities.

Most of my life I have been able to see demons, creatures and entities that belong to a non-physical world and that cause problems for the living who exist in the physical world.

Example
One day in the spring of 2016 I was called from a prison; one of the inmates wanted to speak to me. I accepted and a week later he paid me a visit. He had always been unlucky in his life, unlucky with health, with love, with cars, with work and even with mundane things like light bulbs, which in his house had a considerably shorter lifespan than in other houses. I saw a huge demon lingering in his presence and I advised him to become friends with it.

This is his story:

I am a 37-year-old man and I have been followed and haunted by bad luck my entire life, both concerning machines and health. I know many people that have been successful in life, and I think I have the same qualities as them. If friends have asked for advice, I have freely given it, and if they have followed this advice, things have worked out well for them, but never for me.

My bad luck started from when I was little. The electric cars that I played with did not function. All my toys were ruined. Batteries did not function. When I grew older I started with sports, but was hindered in my training by accidents, diseases and disabilities. I got exhausted, caught the flu and always had problems.

Then I got a motorcycle. It never functioned. Even after being repaired by several garages, it did not work and the faults they found were rare, highly unusual and difficult to repair.

The same with my cars; all three of them were constantly malfunctioning.

The most significant concern was that my health became worse and worse. I had some help from Are Thoresen, but my bad health continued. Then I was put in prison for an offence a friend of mine committed.

I then understood that I had to change something in my life. I asked Are for help, and he saw a huge demon behind my left shoulder. He told me not to try to push it away, but to become friends with it, so I did.

After three days, my life started to change. Light bulbs that always stopped working after just a few days started to shine again. My car started without difficulties. My flu symptoms disappeared. I felt better and better.

Why do some people 'see' such spiritual beings whilst others do not?

This is a very important question. In my early life I thought that everybody could perceive the spiritual world, as I myself had certain abilities that put me in contact with it.

Just lately, I have come to understand the problem of why some can see something, why others see a little more, and why the remainder see nothing. I use the word 'see', although this is not the correct expression for everybody. Some may feel, some may hear and some may taste, even smell, the spiritual world and its spirits. However, for most it is equal to seeing.

The word 'see' is not even correct for those who really can see in the spiritual realm. We do not 'see' with our physical eyes, but with our spiritual eyes. However, as the impression is quite close to the experience of seeing, I will continue to call it 'seeing'.

So how was it that I could see with my spiritual eyes from an early age? It was because I was born with the ability to excarnate from my body, due to my tendency to separate the strong connection between thinking, feeling and will. According to Rudolf Steiner, this is the crucial and most important thing to do if you want to enter the spirit world.

Other 'divisions' within our spiritual body may also be made in order to obtain clairvoyance, such as the division between the physical/etheric bodies and the astral body and the conscious 'I' function. This happens normally during sleep but can also be performed consciously. The peculiar thing is that these innermost parts of the human being—the astral body and the ego—within which we live through what we call 'soul experience', sink down during sleep into an 'indefinite obscurity'. This means simply that this innermost part of the human being needs the stimulus of the external world if it is to be conscious of itself and of the external world. Hence, we can say that at the moment of falling asleep, when this stimulus ceases, man cannot develop consciousness in himself.

If in the normal course of his existence, a human being was able to stimulate the inner parts of his being, to fill them with energy and inner life, then he would become conscious of them. Even if there were no sense-impressions and the sense-bound intellect was inactive and free from the stimulus of the external world, he would then be able to perceive things other than those that come through the stimulus of the senses.

However strange and paradoxical it may sound, it is true that if a person could reproduce a condition which on the one hand resembles sleep and yet is essentially different from it, he could reach supersensible knowledge. His condition would resemble sleep in not depending on any external stimulus; the difference would be that he would not sink into unconsciousness but would unfold a vivid inner life. As may be shown from spiritual-scientific experience, the human being can thus come to clairvoyance. I find it much easier, however, to divide thinking, feeling and will.

The separation of thinking, feeling and will

Rudolf Steiner said that the entanglement of thinking, feeling and will, which are three cosmic and divine forces originating in the spiritual world and not within ourselves, is the main reason why we are anchored in this physical world. I will explain this in more detail, as this is of crucial importance to me and to the readers of this book, especially relating to describing and seeing demons.

When man, consisting of body, soul and spirit, incarnates in the physical world, our feeling, thinking and will are entangled and bound together. The real content, function, power and origin of the three *soul* faculties (thinking, feeling and will) are hidden from us because they overshadow each other. Modern science would have us believe that thinking, feeling and will are just faculties developed or produced by ourselves, and forever interdependent. This is a serious mistake that keeps us in ignorance, in *maya* (or illusion). This is what the characters Morpheus and Neo in the film *The Matrix* call 'the matrix'. It is what we may call the 'greater illusion'.*

It is as if we would believe that colours are within the eye, created by ourselves, and that sounds are within the ear, created by the brain. It is the same with thinking, feeling and will. These are three cosmic forces which we may use as our own, and as such become part of the cosmos, become part of the Divine, part of the spirit world.

We could work wonders—that some people might call magic—if we could separate, or set free from one another, our three soul faculties or powers (thinking, feeling and will).

Will is the strongest but most hidden power.
Feeling is a half-conscious and half-hidden power.
Thinking is the least hidden power.

To be aware of the cosmic origin of these three soul faculties, and to use the immense forces hidden within them in clinical practice, we must learn how to separate them. We can achieve this separation by knowing the secrets of these faculties,† but also through meditation and concentration.

Other ways to separate our three soul faculties are through sunstroke or fainting, through diseases, especially epilepsy or epileptic tendencies, and through death.

For many years, although I never had grand mal convulsions, I thought that I suffered from epilepsy, as the symptoms I had resembled its description so well. Later, I began to doubt that I really had (or have)

---

* The 'lesser illusion' is within the spiritual world itself, when souls abiding there are lost or stuck in the belief that there is no way out, no way to reincarnate, no love and no Christ.
† The knowledge of the true origin of thinking, feeling and will are described by many mystics and in many of the Mysteries through the ages, among others by Rudolf Steiner.

epilepsy. I believe now that it was just spontaneous separation of my thinking, feeling and will in certain situations, probably due to karmic origins.

Spontaneous separation of thinking, feeling and will often, if not always, opens to a spiritual reality, something essential for our spiritual development. On his way to Damascus, Saint Paul (then called Saul) experienced a total opening of the spirit world. In that awakening, he experienced the existence of Christ. St Paul's Epistle to the Galatians (see Galatians 1: 11–16) describes his conversion as a divine revelation in which Jesus Christ appeared to him:

> I want you to know ... that the gospel I preached is not of human origin. I did not receive it from any man, nor was I taught it; rather, I received it by revelation from Jesus Christ. For you have heard of my previous way of life in Judaism, how intensely I persecuted the church of God and tried to destroy it ... But when God ... was pleased to reveal his Son in me so that I might preach him among the Gentiles, my immediate response was not to consult any human being.

However, many doctors attribute Paul's ecstatic vision and conversion to an epileptic fit. For example, in an article entitled 'St Paul and Temporal Lobe Epilepsy' in the *Journal of Neurology, Neurosurgery, and Psychiatry*,[*] we can read the following:

> Evidence is offered to suggest a neurological origin for Paul's ecstatic visions. Paul's physical state at the time of his conversion is discussed and related to these ecstatic experiences. It is postulated that both were manifestations of temporal lobe epilepsy.

Thus, just as they ridicule the Elf School and the Angel School, atheistic doctors ridicule the story of St Paul's spiritual awakening.

From my earliest childhood memories of the phenomenon, the 'symptoms' of 'spontaneous separation' of thinking, feeling and will started with my being unable to judge distances. I did not know how far in the distance objects were. My ability to judge distance slowly disappeared. Depth ceased to have any meaning. The next thing was that width also lost meaning and height disappeared from my consciousness. I felt like I was floating in space, without any dimensions. Then time disappeared. I had no idea in myself how long these instances lasted, although I could see from my watch that they were usually between 30 and 50 minutes. In this way I lost more and more sense of physical

---

[*] 1987, 50(6): 659–664 (PMC1032067).

reality, and then, together with the physical dimensions (depth, width, length and time), my three soul faculties also started to separate and disappear.

My thinking became isolated, my feeling become separated as did my will. At the end of the 'fit', time also ceased to have any meaning. This is much like what Dostoyevsky described in his book, *The Idiot*, as he himself suffered from epilepsy.

For a child of five years, this was frightening. It was like losing the physical world. When I grew older, I found this experience interesting, like a spiritual tour. After experiencing this phenomenon twice a month for 35 years, I decided that I'd had enough. I resolved to treat myself with acupuncture. I had already decided on which point to use, so when the next 'fit' appeared, I inserted the needle. It created an explosion in my brain, as if a jet plane flew right through my head. That was the last fit I ever had. Now, I have been without fits for 30 years.

However, the knowledge of how to separate distance, height, width and time remained. Consequently, I retained the ability of separating thinking, feeling and will. I use this method successfully every time I want to observe energy patterns in patients, trauma within the body or to perceive elemental beings, such as elves, gnomes or demons.

Because of this ability, I quit my ordinary veterinary work soon after qualifying from the Norwegian Veterinary High school (NVH) in Oslo. I started to use acupuncture and pulse diagnosis[*] as my daily tools.

Pulse diagnosis

When I started to teach pulse diagnosis to my students, I thought that it would be easy for them to monitor the pulse-diagnostic patterns in patients. I thought it was just a simple technique. Great then was my surprise when very few were able to master this technique. Why was that?

They did not master pulse diagnosis because they did not enter the spiritual world before monitoring the pulse. After many years, I understood that the preparations for entering the spiritual world, before taking the pulse, was the most important aspect of it. One has to separate feeling, thinking and will to be able to enter the spiritual world and make a proper pulse diagnosis.

---

[*] Pulse diagnosis is a very old method of diagnosing diseases, having been used in China for thousands of years. This method may seem incredible, nonsensical or fraudulent for the Western scientific mind. However, in skilled hands it is a powerful diagnostic method.

Then I 'mingle' the feeling, the consciousness of the heart, the awareness of the blood and the sensitivity of the fingertips to enter the proper pulse diagnosis.

As my path through pulse diagnosis has been of the utmost importance for my understanding of demons, I will take some time to describe this. In my book on alternative veterinary medicine[*] I described the development of my experience of pulse diagnosis, and the consequential findings therein, as follows:

After using pulse diagnosis for 29 years, I realized (in 2009) that the spiritual development I had experienced through using this technique every day had clear and distinct parallels to Rudolf Steiner's description of the path that a spiritual disciple must walk.

A short résumé of my development in pulse diagnosis: In the beginning, the pulse observations were very fragile. I had to be newly washed, in quiet surroundings, not hungry or full, in short, in a balanced state of mind. After some years, this became less and less important as the observations became more and more stable. After additional years, I began literally to see the etheric energy that I detected through the pulse, as if this detection in itself gave rise to the development of spiritual sense organs. First, I saw the etheric energy in and between trees, then in animals and then in humans.

The first observations had their sensory centre in the back of the brain, but then the sensory centre started to wander. First, it wandered towards the heart, then towards the spine and then slowly spread out through the entire body. My observations also became enlarged, from just an intellectual observation to an immediate knowledge of the past, present and future of the observation in question. In addition, the direction of the observation, now having become knowledge, also changed. In the beginning, the direction of the information streamed from the patient to me, but then it started to go both ways, as if the patient also received treatment at the same time that I was diagnosing. The observations also enlarged in space, as they also came to contain the astral part of the patient. I saw his part as an area of flowing light together with the darker etheric energy. Then the observations started to move in time; past, present and future became one.

I found Steiner's description of the development of Inspiration, for example in his book *Occult Science: An Outline*. This was an exact description of what I had experienced since 1980. Although Steiner's

---

[*] *Holistic Veterinary Medicine*, CreateSpace, 2012.

description starts with the development in the astral body, which then spreads to the etheric body, the development through pulse diagnosis starts in the etheric body and then spreads to the astral body.

During my many years of teaching pulse diagnosis, I have totally overestimated my students' abilities to divide their thinking, feeling and will. Because I have had this ability from early in my life, I believed that everybody else also was equipped in the same way. I was wrong!

As I taught the technique to my students, I could not understand that they were unable to see or feel the same as I did. Later, as mentioned above, I understood that pulse diagnosis worked only when the practitioner had already entered the spiritual world, that is, had divided thinking, feeling and will.

For many years, I lectured that the pulse was like a doorway into the 'energetic world'. Now I know that it is a doorway into the spiritual world. However, I also know that this is just a small part of the truth. The pulse is only the tool by which we become aware of the observations we make in the spiritual world. The real doorway is our own mind. That is why the preparations we make before taking the pulse or performing therapy are of crucial importance.

The essential technique or tool to enter the spiritual world, as emphasized above, is to separate thinking, feeling and will.[*] Alternatively, we must separate the dimensions of the physical world into height, width, depth and time.

As feeling is related to depth, the easiest and best way is to start by separating depth from width and height. This is done by a kind of daydreaming, when you merge or wander into the wide expanses of the surroundings. Many experience this state of mind during boring lectures or conversations, when you suddenly fade away and do not really hear what is being said. We must, to enter the spiritual world, develop this art of 'fading away'. Then thinking and will are left behind, and we just float away. We do not think as 'intelligently' as before, and we are unable to 'will' anything. We feel a slight change in the hearing, similar to tinnitus, and the colours of the landscape change a little; a slight turning towards violet.

---

[*] Academically, this change between the non-separation and the separation of the soul faculties is called a 'noetic slippage'. This slippage is a spiritual state where the mind changes between chaos and order, between light and darkness, between the Dionysian and the Apollonian, between the noetic and the chthonic.

In the Elf School* of Reykjavik, Iceland, the teachers use this technique when they prepare to speak with the elves. The students have to fade away into the landscape, i.e., excarnate (go out of the body) slightly. Then the landscape turns somewhat purple, after which the elves appear. Then we *are* in the spiritual world.

The combination of following feeling while being aware of the heart, the blood and the enhanced consciousness of the fingertips, will bring us in an Inspirative connection to the patients, or to whatever else we want to be in connection with.

We must know that the laws in the physical world and the spiritual world differ completely.

- In the physical world, we are bound to the dimensions of space and time, which are interconnected. In the spiritual world this is not so. Time and the three dimensions (length, width and height) are not linked. We can be present in pure thinking, pure feeling and pure will, or in pure time.
- When we then concentrate on a patient, we *are* within that patient, no matter how far away the patient is.
- When we go back in time, as described later, we *are* in the past. Time is not absolute.

How to enter the spiritual world and observe the demons, fairies, elementals and other beings that reside there

1. Feel reverence and respect for the physical world.

First, we must observe the physical world in as detailed a way as possible, and to feel respect for this world.

2. Feel the darkness of the physical world.

We must understand within ourselves that our spirit is not explicable by this world. The spiritual world cannot be found in the physical world. The physical world is 'darkness' in relation to the spirit.

---

*In 2016, the Elf School was 28 years old. What students in the school learn about is related to the 'hidden people'—elves, gnomes, dwarfs, fairies, trolls, mountain spirits, as well as other nature spirits and mythical beings in Iceland and in other countries. The students in the Elf School also learn about the hundreds of Icelanders that have had personal contact with elves. Many of them have been invited into the homes of the elves and the hidden people and have often 'eaten food' there and sometimes have even 'slept' there for one or more nights. The suggestion that the elves and hidden people of Iceland have saved hundreds of lives through the centuries is explored and explained to the students, as well as how this strange friendship between our world and the many other worlds or dimensions can and does exist.

3. *Know yourself as a spiritual being consisting of interconnected thinking, feeling and will.*

We have to feel or understand that in the physical world our thinking, feeling and will are interwoven, are co-dependent. When we think of something, this will immediately influence our feelings and this again will influence what we will.

4. *Accept that as a spiritual being you are different from the physical world.*

At this stage we must feel that we, as *spiritual beings*, are *separated* from the physical world. We should feel as if we are alien to this physical world, as if we have been misplaced, as if we are from somewhere else.

5. *Separate the thinking, feeling and will, and let each go their own way.*

Then we have to fade into the distance, as sometimes happens when we are tired and weary. After a short while, we begin to fade into the surroundings and the words we hear become distant and fuzzy. That is the point we *enter* into the spiritual world, as our thinking, feeling and will start to separate.

6. *By following each of the three soul faculties, we can enter three different areas of the spirit world.*

In the state described above, we must enter each of the three soul faculties individually—into thinking, into feeling and into will. Here it must be emphasized that without a proper training in controlling each of the three soul faculties we are not able to follow them into the spiritual world. In this respect, many 'spiritual travellers' are under a kind of illusion. We have to know ourselves in relation to our thinking, feeling and will in order to be able to travel with them in the spirit land.

7. *Observe all the beings of the spiritual world.*

When we are in the state described above, we now observe that the landscape turns a little purple and starts to become alive. At this point, it is possible to see figures: entities, shapes, demons, elves, streaming snakes or elementals. The entities are often of three different colours: blue, red and yellow (relating to the three soul faculties: blue = thinking, yellow = feeling and red = will). We can also observe a multitude of other beings.

8. *Turn around to see the physical world.*

At this point, we must 'turn around' to observe the physical world that we have just left. We have to do this to 'check' that the splitting of the thinking, feeling and will is stable, i.e. is semi-permanent.

9. *Combine thinking and will (lower abdomen), will and thinking (shoulder area) or will and feeling (heart and arms).*

If we are able to keep the thinking, feeling and will separated whilst looking back at the physical world, we are also able to use our thinking, feeling and will in travelling into the spirit land. We can thus place them together in any combination we want.

10. *Use a combination of will, feeling and intentional thinking to work in the world as a therapist.*

When we let the feeling stream into the patient, we are able to diagnose diseases, or see the demons creating the diseases. If we let our will stream upwards from the feet or the earth and mingle with the feeling through our heart, we are able to perform a very effective treatment in patients. As the power of will (not the egoistic will that we usually think of when we consider will) streams upwards from the feet and the earth, it enters the region of the heart. There the will is transformed by the forces of the heart into a non-egoistic force which can work wonders in a patient when directed by the healing intention streaming downwards from above.

11. *Re-enter the physical world and re-join thinking, feeling and will.*

After having separated thinking, feeling and will, and used them at our demand, we have to re-join them to re-enter the physical world.

12. *Then turn again towards the spiritual world and honour the forces there.*

After re-entering the physical world and re-joining thinking, feeling and will, we have to honour the spiritual world for allowing us to visit. We also may come to understand that thinking, feeling and will are not developed by ourselves, but are forces of the spiritual worlds. They are not our own abilities. They are cosmic forces.

How do we know, and what do we feel, when thinking, feeling and will are separated?

This is a very difficult question, and I can only answer from my own experience, which may or may not reflect the experiences of others. However, my own experiences have been much the same as those who have followed a similar route to myself.

The first indication that separation is occurring is that the surroundings grow a little darker, as when the sun is covered by clouds. This darkness always comes from the right side of my body. Then I experience some difficulty in hearing. Sounds become a little faint, as if I am covered by a thin duvet. Then, as thinking becomes detached, I have to concentrate on 'right thinking' in order to be able to follow the thoughts. In addition, I see clearly that the thoughts are not really mine. The thoughts become isolated. I feel no emotions even if I think of pleasant things.

Then feelings also become isolated. The feelings do not penetrate the body as before and become simple feelings. They do not involve any kind of will. The will also becomes isolated and seems to be of a higher and nobler character, not coloured by my personal desires or wishes.

If I go into each of these three soul faculties, I can experience each of them without interference from the others. Seldom have I experienced *total* division of the three soul forces, but in such moments, thinking, feeling and will become luminescent, almost cosmic.

Example*

Once, while sitting in a car in Ireland, my feeling, thinking and will suddenly and totally separated. It was very unexpected. Flames shot up in the air, changed direction and came directly towards the car. They entered through an open window and made a spiralling movement around me, encircling my head and upper body. I was not burned, nor did I feel any discomfort; I only felt a strange feeling of being invaded by fire. I was transported immediately to another realm of existence.

It is impossible to describe, but this experience was of deep significance and importance, full of meaning that initiated a development that was to continue for many years. I was thrown into a state of complete and total communication with the entire cosmos, on all levels. The thoughts were crystal clear, able to understand everything. The feelings were totally transparent, encompassing all and everything in a love so deep and warm I never thought was possible. The will was as if I could reach the highest mountaintop and overcome the most difficult task. Eventually I came out of this experience and slipped back into the ordinary world, exhilarated and dazed at the totality of such a cosmic experience.

An interesting feature about this experience, and actually all the other 'supernatural' or spiritual experiences described in this book, is that they are impossible to remember exactly. I might put it this way: When I think back on my spiritual experiences, all I remember is the impressions I had after the experience was over, after it had ended. I never remember the actual experience in detail. I do have a recollection of some of the pictures, of the insights, but the details have vanished as if it were a dream. This fact leaves me with an uncertainty, a feeling that it did not really

---

*This is described in my book, *Forgotten Mysteries of Atlantis*, CreateSpace 2015.

happen, that it was only a memory of something else. However, when I focus on the situation and relive the experience, feeling the huge impression it left upon my soul, I have never doubted that what I experienced was real.

This 'forgetting' all details of what happens when I am in the spiritual world can also be a problem in my work as a healer and veterinarian. I always make a pulse diagnosis of my patients, but immediately after I forget the results. Often this forgetfulness makes the patients and/or animal-owners irritated, but there is nothing I can do about it.

Concerning the mystery of going into the dimension of 'depth'

As you will now understand, the separating of thinking, feeling and will is of the utmost importance for the ability of entering into the spiritual world. 'Fading into the distance' is the most important aspect of this process. It can be achieved in several ways, using the eyes, the mind, the memory or the other senses:

Using meditation. This is of course an old and acknowledged method and contains all the other methods here described. Through meditation, we may fade into different aspects of reality as we shut down our thinking. This brings us into the spiritual world through various door-ways, some better and some worse. We must stop the thinking and in the same moment put the other senses to the side. Often at this stage certain numbness is felt in the body, especially in the area of the shoulders. The eyes of the mind are then activated and forms and Imaginations become stronger. We have entered the spiritual world.

Using the eyes. We then have to focus on what we see, especially what we can see in the distance. We concentrate our sight on a spot or an object and try to fade into this point or object. At this time, the hearing and the mind join with the eyes in fading away, and sounds, sights and consciousness become distant. In this state, we are free to enter the spiritual world and can travel in space and time in both our thoughts, our feelings and in our will.

Using the memory. We then have to 'shut down' all our senses along with the active mind. We fade into an old and pleasant memory and we are 'transported' to this distant place or incident. We leave behind our conscious thinking, feeling and will, and merge totally with the memory. This has been described as the 'meditation of daydreaming'.

Using the feeling of touch. This is more difficult than the other methods. You may get a slight concept of this if you remember an instance when you were sitting alone with your loved one, and s/he was carefully touching and stroking your hand. The feeling of touch then carried you away, into a state of bliss and comfort.

Using our ears. This is a method that can be used in connection to spiritual music and is used by many people, consciously or unconsciously. This is the reason why you may feel calmed or spiritualized by listening to certain kinds of music. When we listen to calm and spiritual music, we may fade out into eternity. The feelings take over and thinking is diminished.

Using concentration. This method is described in 'Goethean meditation', as known in anthroposophy. In this meditation, we actually use some of the other methods here described. When we use our concentration as a means to fade into eternity, we should concentrate on a chosen object and hold this concentration for as long a time as possible.

Example
I was 21 years old, sitting painting in the high mountains of Norway. I painted a little creek and concentrated my eyes and my whole mind on the creek, trying to put the impressions of running water on to the canvas. To do this I used about one hour of deep concentration. At a certain moment, the painting was finished. I then 'came out of or back from' the concentration, and immediately went deep into the spiritual world. The whole mountain, including its plants, started to sing, and heavenly music filled the air. I then heard songs and melodies that I was later able to write down and play on my guitar.

Using the inward way. It is of great importance to know that all the 'methods' described above also may be performed by going inward. Outwardly, you will find the outer world, and inwardly you will find the inner world.

Both seeing with the eyes, hearing with the ears and concentration— yes, even the mind and memory, touch and meditation—all have two directions in which to go: outward (and back in time) as described, or inward (and forward in time).

Chapter One

Are Demons Real?—Personal Experiences

Are demons real, or are they just what could be characterized as 'bad energies', subconscious pathological patterns, neuroses, psychoses, hallucinations or any other inventions of the mind?

I am painfully aware that if I called demons 'pathological, noxious structures within the mind'—structures that have a life of their own, are able to move within the body and even jump onto other living beings—I would avoid much discussion and criticism.

However, I cannot do this without lying to myself! If we take seriously what so many alternative therapists, veterinarians or doctors experience, then we must call them *demons*. These pathological structures behave like conscious entities. They move around in the body, they jump from body to body and they may change behaviour (symptoms). They may even leave their host and return after some months. They can go back in time, 'remember' old symptoms, and display several other qualities that belong to creatures of the spiritual world.

These structures do have a conscious life; therefore, I will call them demons. In addition, I have seen these entities more or less throughout my whole life.

Example
As described earlier, I saw my teacher's head surrounded by a strong light, and in this light, the date of his death was written. This ability to see 'death dates' lasted for some months and then vanished. There is a law in the spiritual world that nothing is lost, it just transforms. Abilities that have been lost always reappear. Just a few months ago, in the spring of 2016, this ability to see the 'death date' turned up again, but in quite another way. It reappeared in an upgraded version, similar to an upgraded computer program.

I do not see the death date as such now. The date is 'material based' and is an illusion. Now I see death itself in the form of a demon, spirit or an elemental being, and I can see how close death is to the physical body. The further away it is, the longer the time before death; the closer it is, the nearer death is.

How to perceive spiritual beings

Before going into a more detailed description of the various types of demons, I would like to say something about how to perceive spiritual beings in general.

Spiritual beings are usually seen with the *spiritual eye* and cannot be seen with the physical eyes. They cannot be seen as we see ordinary objects in the physical world. They must be seen through a 'will' to see them. This needs some explanation.

When we stand in the midst of a forest in the physical world, we can look calmly and see all the trees and bushes, birds and bees that are around us. This is not so in the spiritual world. In this world, we must know what to look for and want to see what we know. We have to see spiritual beings in a 'knowing-and-wanting-to-see' way. We must *want* to see the elves, that we already know of, before they appear in front of our eyes (after we have separated our thinking, feeling and will, of course). This means that if we have no knowledge of the spiritual world and do not know what to look for, and don't want to see what we know, then we will see nothing at all. Thus, if we do not already know of the existence of elves, we will not be able to see them.

When we have become aware of and 'seen' certain spiritual beings, then we can build upon this knowledge the next time we perceive them. It is much like learning a skill that requires practice.

Let us, for example, look at learning to play an instrument. We first learn the fundamentals, such as starting to know the placement of the fingers on the piano. The next step is learning to play the scales. Then after a while, we suddenly understand the scales and are able to change between the keys. It is in the same way that we perceive the spiritual world. We go further and further in seeing and understanding each time we enter the spiritual world.

However, sometimes spiritual vision is so vital and strong that it is difficult to tell if we see with our spiritual or with our physical sense organs. The more important the message brought forward by the spiritual world, the more 'physical' the image becomes.

Several examples of this can be found in the Bible, when important messages of great significance for the Jewish people were proclaimed from the spiritual world. I refer in particular to the prophets, the births of both John the Baptist, Jesus and several other instances.

Example 1

One time I was on my way out of a Norwegian fjord, to place my boat on land for the winter. [*] *The route I had to sail was out into the open sea, passing a rocky area, and then into a quiet fjord (Sandefjordsfjorden), where the boat was intended to rest over the winter. As I sailed the boat out into the sea, the wind became stronger and*

---

[*] This incident is described in detail in my book, *The Forgotten Mysteries of Atlantis*, CreateSpace 2015.

stronger and the boat was lifted up by the swell of the peaking waves, crashing down into the troughs. The engine worked hard, and the small 23-foot wooden boat rocked in the rough sea. The weather became more and more hostile, turning stormy, but I persevered. After a while, I reached the most dangerous part of the route. Then something totally unexpected and unbelievable happened. A huge hand appeared out of the sea, coming up from the depths. The water was running down its skin and seaweed was hanging from its fingers. It was a totally real and physical hand, apart from the fact that it was around eight to ten metres high. No upper arm was to be seen, no body, no head, no face, just this enormous hand. Then the hand started slowly to beckon me, as if it wanted me to follow, asking me to come down into the depths of the ocean. I was well acquainted with old Scandinavian folklore and immediately understood that it was the 'Hand of Draugen', calling me to my death by drowning. (In Norse mythology, 'Draugen' is the malevolent ghost of a sailor who drowned at sea. The ghost tries to lure other sailors to their deaths).

In a flash, I instantly realized my predicament and, without hesitation or fear, made a quick decision. I turned the boat and sailed back with the wind to the summer-anchor place. As I travelled with the waves and the wind, this part of the journey took only a short time, perhaps 15 minutes.

A few days later, when the weather was calm and still once again, I made a second attempt to sail the boat to its intended winter place. After just ten minutes the engine stopped. There was no more fuel! I had totally forgotten to check the level of the gas. If I had continued on route that stormy day, the fuel would have run out exactly at the most dangerous part of the journey. The boat would surely have been destroyed, splintering on the rocks and sinking. I would have been lucky to survive. My knowledge of the 'Hand of Draugen' had saved my life.

Example 2

It is not only when the situation is important or dangerous for the people involved that the perception of spiritual beings becomes very apparent, almost physical; it is also when the situation is important for the elementals or spiritual beings themselves.

Once when walking in the forest I came across a woman sitting beside a tree, weeping. Two men stood by her side trying to comfort her but she was inconsolable. She was weeping for the trees. I understood after some time that they were not real humans, but 'hulder' or 'huldr', * *and she was being comforted by two 'huldre-***

---

* A *hulder* is a seductive forest creature found in Scandinavian folklore. (Her name derives from a root meaning 'covered' or 'secret'.) In Norwegian folklore, she is known as *huldra*. She is also known as the *skogsrå* (forest spirit) or *Tallemaja* (pine tree Mary) in Swedish folklore, and *ulda* in Sámi folklore. Whereas the female hulder is almost invariably described as incredibly, seductively beautiful, the males of the same race are often said to be hideous, with grotesquely long noses.

kalls', *as described in Nordic mythology. I also tried to comfort her, but then all three disappeared. I was not supposed to see them, as this matter did not concern me.*

The next week, huge machines came and cut down the old forest.

I almost cried.

Experiences as a veterinarian

Most animal owners and veterinarians, including myself, have observed that pet dogs and cats often seem to 'take over' the diseases of their owners.

If you master pulse diagnosis, you will see that most of the diseases in domesticated animals such as cows, horses, sheep and all pets originate in man, in the human being.

I once attended a course for anthroposophic doctors in Chechia, and the doctor organizing the course said in his introduction, '. . . We now know that 80% of all diseases in children originate in the parents, in the adults.' In my mind I added, '. . . and 80% of all diseases in animals'. For me this was an important message.

The doctor then said: '. . . and furthermore, 80% of all diseases in grown-ups originate from men and women not understanding each other. To summarize, misunderstanding between men and women is the origin of 80% of all disease in both adults and in children. I also find that most diseases in animals are man-made or are transmitted from their owners or handlers. *Mars must come to understand Venus and vice versa.*

When we have accepted that 80% of all disease in both children and animals originates in men and women (something which I have seen from the very beginning of my veterinary practice in 1979), we might ask for the *mechanism* behind this 'crossing over' of disease from people to children and to animals.

At first, I imagined this 'crossing over' as a sort of transference of a contagious agent. Then I imagined it as a sort of 'induction', through some kind of electromagnetic radiation. Then I imagined it as a kind of influence arising from the human astral body. In a way, this is true. The astral bodies of all humans do influence each other and the animals attached to them. However, the pathological influence is mediated through luciferic demonic elementals.

Then I imagined it as a kind of influence issuing from the human etheric body. In a way, this is also true, as the etheric bodies of all humans do influence each other and animals, as described by Rudolf Steiner in my Preface. However, the pathological influence is also mediated here through elemental beings of an ahrimanic and demonic character.

I realized that it was the demon of the disease that multiplied and spread.

When I understood this and directed my spiritual sight towards the owners and the animals, it was easy to see the demons.

Let us consider a disease such as the common flu. It spreads to (almost) all people. Everyone who becomes infected gets a 'personal' demon. The main demon of the disease multiplies and divides to infect all those that have a weakness in one of their energetic bodies (etheric, astral or 'I'), through which the demon may enter. If there are no weaknesses, the person in question does not get the disease.

The demon multiplies, especially if it is partially driven out with the help of allopathic remedies or symptomatic treatment. After a while, it returns to the original person, multiplies and influences other members of the household and the animals they are attached to.

This 'driving out and multiplying' is described in detail in the Bible, for example in Matthew 12: 43–45, where it says:

When an unclean spirit goes out of a man, he goes through dry places, seeking rest, and finds none. Then he says, 'I will return to my house from which I came.' And when he comes, he finds it empty, swept, and put in order. Then he goes and takes with him seven other spirits more wicked than himself, and they enter and dwell there; and the last state of that man is worse than the first. So, shall it also be with this wicked generation.

This passage therefore describes in detail the expulsion of demons, only to have them return and multiply later:

Another description in the Bible (Luke 8: 27–40) reads:

When He stepped out on land, a man from the city who had demons for a long time met Him. He wore no clothes, nor did he live in a house but in the tombs. When he saw Jesus, he cried out and fell down before Him, and with a loud voice said, 'What have You to do with me, Jesus, Son of the Highest God? I plead with You, do not torment me.' For He had commanded the unclean spirit to come out of the man. It often had seized him, and he was kept under guard, bound with chains and shackles. But he broke the shackles and was driven by the demon into the wilderness.

Jesus asked him, 'What is your name?'

He said, 'Legion', because many demons had entered him. And they begged Him not to command them to go out into the abyss.

There was a large herd of swine feeding on the mountain. They begged Him to permit them to enter them, and He permitted them. Then the demons went out of the man and entered the swine, and the herd ran violently down the steep bank into the lake and was drowned.

When those who fed them saw what had happened, they fled and reported it in the city and in the country. Then they went out to see what had happened, and came to Jesus, and found the man from whom the demons had departed sitting at the feet of Jesus, clothed, and in his right mind. And they were afraid. Those who had seen it told them how he who had been possessed by demons was healed. Then the whole crowd from the surrounding country of the Gadarenes asked Him to depart from them, for they were seized with great fear. So, He went into the boat and returned.

Now the man from whom the demons had departed asked Him if he could stay with Him. But Jesus sent him away, saying, 'Return to your own house, and tell what great things God has done for you.' So, he went his way and proclaimed throughout the whole city what great things Jesus had done for him.

What happens when ahrimanic and luciferic demons 'enter' the human body (or when ordinary elementals are transformed to demonic ones)

When *ahrimanic* demons enter or are created in the body, the results are always negative. How they affect us depends a lot on our personal weak areas. If for example they enter into the *physical body* we become physically sick, our blood circulation is hindered, we are without life and energy, we become sclerotic and old. If they enter into the *soul*, we become bound-up with cold emotions, interested in money and adapt an ignorant perspective on life, especially towards other people's sufferings. If they enter into the *spirit* we become ignorant towards the spiritual world, atheistic, hostile and in denial of religious belief.

Ahrimanic elementals that enter the demonic realm cause us to be without empathy (think of our present-day governments, or the 'big pharma' industry), showing extreme intelligence and an over-interest in 'artificial intelligence'. In addition, they cause degenerative diseases (calcification, arteriosclerosis, stiff joints and depression). A darker and more dangerous class of ahrimanic demon is the azuric one. The azuric elementals, when entering the demonic realm, cause us to lose our higher self, our higher 'I', leaving us with only our lower 'I', and as such we become egoistic and influenced by ahrimanic knowledge that can be detrimental to human evolution. When *luciferic* demons enter us, the effect is that we become self-occupied, uninterested in our fellow human beings and with no curiosity in our earthly surroundings.

If, for example, they enter into the *physical body*, we get pain and infections; we become feverishly sick. If they enter into the *soul*, we become bound-up with negative emotions, such as greed, jealousy or anger. We also get inflated thoughts about ourselves. We show a strong tendency towards self-aggrandizement. If they enter into the *spirit*, we become confused, depressed and lose the way on our spiritual path. We have the tendency to become convinced by all kinds of spiritual movements. This can be seen very clearly in India where whole lives, en masse, are dedicated to the worship of the old luciferic-orientated gods (that were appropriate 2,000 years ago but not today), but little concern is focused on the immediate surroundings relating to garbage, air pollution, the suffering of animals, children and women.

Luciferic elementals that enter the demonic realm cause us to become obsessed and manic (think of crazy football fans or 'Black Friday' shoppers) or become swept-away artistically (producing art that has nothing to do with reality), egoistic and self-occupied. In addition, they cause painful conditions such as rheumatism, chronic pain, headaches and infections. Hysteria and addictions are diagnoses that would also come under luciferic influence.

Meetings with the icelandic elves and the 'hidden people'

Together with a spiritually minded group consisting of 35 holistic veterinarians, I visited Iceland in 2017. While travelling the northern part of this amazing country, I had the good fortune to meet the elders of both an elf tribe and of two tribes of the 'hidden people'. I was initiated in three parts of their history and lives, namely their creation story, their future and their cosmology or world view.

So, what do the elves and the 'hidden people' look like? How can they be addressed and how do they respond? To be able to see these etheric/astral creatures, we must first enter the spiritual realm by dividing our thinking, feeling and will. Then, a certain movement appears when we turn our spiritual eyes towards the natural world. When we use our third eye, we see nature elementals and when we use the eye of our heart we see many more.

As the creation of the elves originates in the spiritual and cosmic forces of thinking, feeling and will, they are mainly of three kinds: the blue ones are related to thinking, the yellow ones to feeling and the red ones to the strong force of will. As these three forces of the cosmos also are responsible for all-natural laws, the red elves are connected to gravity as gravity is derived from cosmic will. The red elves are therefore heavier than the others.

There are elves of all sizes. Some are as big as humans, some as small as tiny flowers. The 'hidden people' are mostly like human beings, although some families look more like older human species, such as the Neanderthals. The elves are dressed in colours but the 'hidden people' are dressed in grey clothes, mostly in fashion of around two hundred years ago. These entities talk to you in Imaginations, not human words. Rudolf Steiner says that they have no incarnated 'I' and that their physical body is in the astral world with their consciousness in the physical world (that is, in our world).

I was told the following Creation Story by the elves. In the first beginning, the humans, together with the whole world, existed only in the spiritual realm, in the etheric and astral. To be able to enter or penetrate into the material realm, it was necessary to make a division in the etheric, just as God made a split in the waters on the second day of Creation. One part was kept in the etheric and one part was expelled into the material realm.

As a consequence of this split, the material world became like a mirror image, a reflection of the etheric. That is why humans always see the etheric phenomena as if turned the other way around, as in a mirror. However, it is really the material world that is the 'wrong way around', as it were. This split is seen today in embryology, in the turning of the foetus in the third week. As the cosmic etheric forces are threefold, constituted of thinking, feeling and will, the elves are likewise split into three groups, although they cooperate perfectly. The blue elves are masters of spiritual thinking, the yellow ones of feeling and the red ones of will.

Both elves and humans are trapped in their own worlds: elves in the etheric realm and humans in the material realm. The only way to redemption and liberation for both sides is for humans to spiritualize all powers and forces within their thinking, feeling and will, so that both sides or worlds may reunite. Otherwise the elves will remain stuck in the etheric world.

If human beings don't spiritualize their thinking, feeling and will, then the etheric beings will be stuck in their etheric world, the humans in their material world and the animals will also be stuck at their level of development. The whole cosmos is thus dependent of the spiritualization of man. To be able to do this, Christ is absolutely necessary. This future is not possible without the help and sacrifice which Christ made on Golgotha. This act helps man to create a new spiritual centre in the body, a new chakra; not the old one, related to the spinal up-rising stream and neither the one in front of the heart, but the one just below and behind the heart, which can be reached only by passing the heart and then turning back. This is the great mystery of 'the turning back'.

As described above, the human realm or world appears inverted or upside-down compared to the etheric realm. Although we see the elves as standing on the ground, they really don't touch our world with the soles of their feet. They are actually upside-down. Our planet is their heaven and our cosmos is their planet or ground.

We experience the same thing when we die. Our interior becomes the whole cosmos and the whole cosmos becomes our interior. That the cosmos appears endless is therefore an illusion of the material world. This illusion of endlessness is created by the fact that both the etheric and the physical cosmos are created or organized as a mixture of fractals, holistic constructions and a hall of mirrors, both in themselves and between each other. There are two areas of this fractal world that differ, according to the elves: the luciferic area, where all mirrors reflect everything back and thus appear very shiny, and Ahriman's Eighth Sphere, where darkness reigns. Here all the mirrors are turned inward.

During the time we spent on Iceland, we became unpleasantly aware of an increasing problem for the elves and the 'hidden people'. This was the massive infiltration and invasion of 'orchs' (or jotuns, as the Vikings called this species of ahrimanic beings). The ever-increasing materialism of humanity in general, and the astonishing egoism of tourists in parti-cular, attracts and creates these beings, which cause great suffering in the etheric realm.

When I was visiting this huge 'city' of 'hidden people', they used the energy and respect that our group brought with them to move or escape the ahrimanic invasion and resettle in an area where this invasion had, until now, been kept at bay. In this new area, the etheric beings already living there had succeeded in creating a magic wall against the 'jotnic' invasion. It was very interesting to see how frustrated the jotuns or orchs were when they met this impenetrable wall.

A shamanistic approach

A genuine shaman works consciously with spirits. The question is, what sort of spirits are they? Are they higher spirits, with which pre-Christian priests worked, or are they nature spirits, plant spirits, tree spirits or animal spirits? Are they demons or angels?

I have known several shamans and have been involved with and witnessed several shamanistic sessions and gatherings. I have seen many spirits attracted and/or used by the shamans, so before answering the questions posed above, I will describe two instances. Both occurred during the shaman gatherings organized by Ailo Gaup, held at Harestua, north of Oslo, in Norway in 2012 and 2013.

Example 1

We stood in a large circle of about 60 people, all of us more or less open to what was going on, more or less open to the reality of shamanism. We were there to perform rituals. The first one to perform a ritual was Ailo Gaup, a male Norwegian shaman of Sami origin. (The Sami live in the arctic woods and tundra in the northern parts of Norway, Sweden, Finland and Russia. They are very hardy people, who farm reindeer and survive in a very harsh climate. Fish also are important in their diet.) He began with ritual drumming and sing-ing in the typical Sami way called 'joik'.* While he was doing his ritual, sev-eral of the Norwegian elemental nature spirits had emerged from the forest and stood around the circle of participants. The elementals look very much like goblins, 'forest goblins' or 'skog nisser', as they are called in Norwegian lan-guage and tradition. The 'skog nisser' enjoyed the ritual and were willing to engage in human affairs—if asked. Then a shaman from South America, who was a guest at the gathering, made his ritual. This was quite similar to the Sami one, but must have been quite different also, because totally different spirits were attracted. A huge anaconda appeared. I was actually a bit frigh-tened, but after reminding myself that this was all in the realm of the spiritual, I relaxed. The anaconda curled around the whole circle, thrilled by the ritual of the South American shaman. But then something unexpected happened. When the Norwegian goblins, the 'skog-nisser,' saw the anaconda they were very frightened and retreated into the forest. They simply disappeared.†

---

* A *joik* (also spelled yoik), *luohti*, *vuolle*, *leu'dd*, or *juoiggus* is a traditional Sami form of song. According to the oral tradition, the fairies and elves of the arctic land gave yoiks to the Sámi People. The sound of joik is comparable to the traditional chanting of some Native American cultures, but non-verbal singing as such is by no means limited to these cultures. With the Christianization of the Sami, joiking was condemned as sinful.

† Later I brought up the question to the Norwegian shaman of mixing rituals and the experience of the frightened goblins. I expressed my opinion that it might be wrong to mix different shamanistic rituals, as seems to be the trend today. This is important as today shamans from all over the world, North and South America, Africa, Mongolia and Scandinavia meet to discuss common issues. They then often perform their individual cultural rituals. The effect of this will be interesting to follow and observe.

Example 2

The second instance occurred when Anette Høst, *a Danish shaman, demonstrated 'seiðr'.* * *This is an old method of coaxing elemental spirits to work for you. Before the ritual or the seiðr was performed, we all discussed which intention or instruction we should give the elementals. The group of participants decided that they wanted the building of a planned power plant, which was to be situated on a holy Sami mountain up north, to be stopped or hindered. This ritual was performed through singing. The shaman sat in the middle of the ring of participants (I was one of them), and both she and the participants sang. After a short while a portal opened in the etheric realm, just to the left of the shaman. To me, it appeared almost physical in nature. The portal looked like an open spiral, similar to looking into the shell of a huge snail. In this portal I clearly saw two entities (whenever I have seen portals, I have always seen two entities within them). They looked like typical elementals, rather ugly, like small 'trolls'. They were definitely elementals with a demonic tendency. Then the shaman gave them an order to somehow stop the building of the power plant in question. They were infused by the will, energy and intention of the shaman together with the 'song energy' of the surrounding circle. The elementals received the instructions she gave to them and they became even more demonic in appearance.*

This reminded me of black magic, and I felt a little uncomfortable being part of this.

Ganning/Ganding

Ganding, or 'casting spells', is a derivation of an ancient Nordic word which was linked to the Norse *seiðr*. In effect it is quite like *seiðr*, as in both traditions and practices elementals (nature spirits) are used to perform deeds or actions and as such are often used in the form of demons (performing ill deeds, hurting people or animals).

From the 1500s, the word has been used in relation to witchcraft and magic performed by the Sami. Medieval sources mention only the word g*andra* which was used to describe a spiritual envoy, often sent in a trance, who could accomplish all sorts of errands such as obtaining information and/or doing people harm. The words *sorcery* and the verb g*ande* seem to have evolved from a common root in the late Middle Ages. It is likely that g*andra* originally derives from *stake* (to run with).

---

* *Seiðr* (sometimes anglicized as *seidhr, seidh, seidr, seithr, seith or seid*) is an Old Norse term for a type of sorcery which was practiced in Norse society during the Late Scandinavian Iron Age. Connected with Norse religion, its origins are largely unknown, although it gradually eroded following the Christianization of Scandinavia. Various scholars have debated the nature of seiðr, some arguing that it was shamanic in context, involving visionary journeys by its practitioners.

In folk tradition from the 1500s onwards, there was much talk about 'sorcery', but the meaning changed from 'spiritual envoy', which is not bad, to something which only did harm. Sorcery became synonymous with enchanted sticks, twigs, arrows, hairballs, (sorcery) flies and other methods. Sami shamans, especially, could 'shoot' or send such 'bulkheads' to act against humans and animals and cause them accidents, illness or death.

In Norse times and in north Norwegian folklore *Gandferd* was a witch riding on the *Åsgårds-rei* through the air. Gandferda could also be understood as a 'storm' of ghosts, while the word *'gandreið'* meant that the demons were riding the air.

How to hinder demons from entering us

Follow the Eightfold Path of Buddha
This concerns the teaching of Buddha to his disciples to develop the right view, the right resolve, the right word, the right action, the right standpoint, the right effort, the right remembrance and the right contemplation. If followed, he said, it would gradually lead to the extinction of the thirst for existence with its attendant suffering and impart to the soul something that brings liberation from elements from past lives that enslave it.[*]

Develop a strong consciousness of the self, of the 'I AM'
The consciousness of the 'I AM' is the light that leads us out of error and corruption, the light that enables us to find our way past both the ahrimanic and the luciferic demons.

If we ask ourselves what was lost to humanity when the 'I' descended from the spiritual world and became ensnared by desires and cravings under the influence of Lucifer, and then, under Ahriman's influence, became lost in the earthly, physical world of lies, error and illusion, the answer is that man lost his direct connection to the spiritual world. He lost his understanding of the spiritual world and how it operates. I strongly believe that this spiritual connection must somehow be re-found. If not, we will become slaves trapped under the influences of Lucifer and Ahriman.

Adversary elementals can enter man on many different levels. The further into the body they reach, the more damage is done. The first 'step'

---

[*] There are many books on this subject. See for example, *The Eightfold Path* by Joop van Dam, Temple Lodge Publishing 2016.

is the astral body, or in some cases the etheric body. The next step is the etheric body, and the last step is the physical body, although some may say that the 'I' is the last and most dangerous step.

There is much more on these themes later in the book.

Chapter Two

How are Demons Created? Earth Radiation

Demons can be divided into two groups, according to when and how they are created:

1. Demons created by human actions.
2. Demons existing from earlier cosmic development.

I find it extremely difficult to make a differentiation between these two groups as they appear equal, although I know that they are different.

Demons are always involved in the development of disease, both in animals and in man. Concerning diseases in humans relating to both the body and the soul, the most significant demons are those we have created through our deeds, thoughts and feelings. They may be called 'karmic' demons.

Example

I was visiting a friend of mine. He was often thrown into severe depression and could not work for weeks or months. He had no idea where this depression came from. At the time I was visiting him, he was having a better period. I sat at the table, and he went to the kitchen to make me a coffee. Then a huge and dark shadow slowly engulfed him, and he sank into a dark mood. This dark mood that descended upon him was the cause of his repeated depression, and was caused by this huge, dark demon. I tried to ask the demon from whence it came, but it would not answer. I continued to ask the entity how old it was, and finally it responded that it had been created by a dark action committed by my friend's grandfather. The action had to do with an act of low morality.

The next step would be to find out what this was, and then ask for forgiveness. If this is performed properly, the demon would disperse and vanish, having been freed and transformed. We must not just push the demon away. It wants to be transformed.

Demons and earth radiation

Another semi-physical expression of created demons is so-called 'earth radiation'. This etheric force from the depths of the earth is very central to understanding demons, ahrimanic beings and disease. Therefore, it will be dealt with now at some length.

This requires an introduction and explanation. My development in seeing and understanding earth radiation resembles my path in seeing and understanding pathological demons. This is the first indication that they belong together, that they are one and the same.

Since 1972, I have been investigating so-called ley lines and earth grids, also called earth radiation—especially since 2004, when I have been able to see this matrix of energy.[*] This energy is spiritual energy, because as yet no one has been able to prove its existence using electronic instruments or other kinds of devices. It can be detected only by living beings.

I am aware that there is also a huge grid of electromagnetic energy that causes disease in living beings, especially that which is emitted by high-voltage installations and cell phones. This is something I will come back to later, but here I will write about the 'energetic grid', which has a spiritual origin.

This spiritual energy is an emanation from the demonic layers of the earth itself. It is also, at the same time, an expression of the ahrimanic entities created by human misdeeds from all times. This 'spiritual substance' is thus both the demonic entities themselves and a kind of fuel or food for the ahrimanic entities, including 'the doppelgänger'.

This emanation fuels the karmic demons and causes disease, especially if one sleeps above such radiation or is connected to it.

I have evaluated the work and efficacy of many who attempt to stop or divert this spiritual earth radiation. Incurably sick people, who want to see if they can become better after this type of radiation is removed, usually summon such 'radiation stoppers'.

The radiation stoppers' attempt to find the radiation using different methods such as a pendulum or a divining rod, and by means of different copper threads, symbols, mental imaging or other devices. However, the success of such devices to divert the radiation usually lasts only some days, weeks or months. The radiation then changes in some way, so that the dowsers have to come back once a month or so. My conclusion from these observations is that this matrix or grid of earth radiation is changeable: it is alive and it has its own intent.

The next level of my observations is as follows: I have discovered that the lines of earth radiation not only change, but also move several metres by themselves, especially if someone tries to alter, disperse or stop them. Then I made the astonishing observation that they could also be moved by my own will and intent.

---

[*] As described in my book *Holistic Veterinary Medicine* and also in my book, *Poplar* (both CreateSpace).

I started to demonstrate this to dowsers. During a congress, I moved a ley line so fast that many of the participants felt it like a soft wind that swept through the room. I perform this moving of the earth radiation according to the following method: First, I have to 'see' the energetic lines.[*] After seeing the energy, I hold it with my will power, just as we may hold a naughty child when we want attention or when we want the child to act a certain way. Then I move the energies by willpower and intent to another place. They follow my command and move.

I have used this method several times. During a veterinary acupuncture course in Germany, the leader of the German dowsers' association was to demonstrate how to find 'earth radiation lines'. She had dowsed an area of the forest beforehand and had found radiation lines there. Her task was to show the class how to find them and then mark them with coloured paper.

I stood watching from a distance. Just before she was ready to demonstrate the presence and effect of the lines to the group, I moved all the lines away. Then I waited for the results. She started to look for the lines, but she could not find any. She became very frustrated. Then I knew that my vision and actions were objective. This led me to understand that the 'earth radiation lines' were living entities that could be manipulated by my will, which means through the spirit.

For years, I investigated the 'black snakes' that I saw in nature. One peculiarity regarding them was that they opened my mind to time itself. They did not only stream between trees and other living entities, but they also streamed between past and present and between present and future. I discovered that I could travel 'inside' them to the past (always towards the left) or into the future (always to the right). If we do not enter the 'snakes' deeply but stay in the periphery, the directions of time are opposite.

To travel 'out of the body' in time and space, shamans of the Sami people and other indigenous cultures project their spirit into 'benevolent spirit guides'. The 'black snakes' are my guides. When I travel within them into the past or the future, it must rather be described as if the past or the future comes towards me. When the past comes into my consciousness, it is like an encounter with an ahrimanic demon or spirit.

---

[*] Earth radiation is 'seen' (at least I understand it this way) as snakes traversing the room, or the forest, black and shiny, going from left to right or from right to left. One direction goes from the past to the future and the other direction goes from the future to the past. At a certain level, this energy has the shape of a snake; on a higher level, it has the shape of a demon. Before 2014, I saw demons in the shape of snakes and mainly as 'earth radiation'. Lately I can see them as demons, clinging to humans, causing diseases and pain, depression or anger. Even death can be seen in this way.

When the future comes into my consciousness, it is like an encounter with a luciferic demon or spirit. I seldom dare to travel to the future!

When my consciousness encounters these two time streams, one from the past and one from the future, I face the 'double stream' of time. This is a very important and hidden mystery. I will not discuss it further in this book, except to say that it can be met within the elemental world of the trees.

When I travel inside these streams into the past, I experience strange and changing plant-forms—plant-forms that have not been seen for millions of years. With this travelling technique, I can investigate the leaf forms as far back as ancient Silurian times.*

Once I totally lost myself when travelling back in time. I can usually step out of the described 'streaming black snakes' easily, but this one time it was impossible. I disappeared into the past. I opened my physical eyes wide open, but still I could not see the present. I was really stuck in the past. I saw, with open eyes, the dinosaurs walking past me, just as if I was actually there (which I believe I really was). I saw the old forms of trees and plants growing around me and I was taken further and further back in time. I started to become scared. I tried several methods to come back to the present time but was totally unable to do so. After a long while I managed to come back, using old Sámi rituals as a help.

Then I started to understand how this darker grid or matrix of 'snakes' is created. They are all caused by the evil or egoistic deeds of humans and fed by the upward streaming forces of the deeper layers of the Earth. If the human being that created any particular elemental demon is dead, the grid-line remains. During this period, it may cause disease or discomfort in other humans or animals that happen to sleep or live where the lines are. In a later life, when the maker of the line is reincarnated, the spirit of this reincarnated human is drawn to the site where the line awaits. When he or she then comes again to the area of past sin, the grid-lines (demons) attach to the human who then remembers the past deeds. It is known within criminology that the perpetrator always returns to the scene of the crime.

If they are benevolent, the lines are elementals. If they are malevolent, they are demons, although both are connected to our karma. If their makers are in the other world, the demons may haunt other people whilst they await the rebirth of their 'makers'.

---

*The Silurian time is a geological period and system that extends from the end of the Ordovician Period, 443.8 million years ago, to the beginning of the Devonian Period, 419.2 million years ago.

These lines or grids contain the whole history of our lives. As such, they may be called the Akashic Chronicle.[*] Karma and the Akashic Chronicle are interwoven in this grid, and as such are two parts or realities of the same grid.

The whole world is full of these demons, these demonic grids, fed by the upward streaming of ahrimanic forces from the depths. They are of many kinds and appearances. Some are made by greed, some from anger, murder, violence, jealousy, pain or sorrow.

In the Old Norse book *Edda*[†] a similar structure or phenomenon is described, relating to the *Norns*.[‡] The Old Vikings 'saw' that when a child was born, a 'web' was waiting for it. Three women connected the child to this web, which was the karma of the little child. The names of the three women were Past, Present and Future (*Vilje, Ve* and *Verdande*). The *Norns* also had a scissor to cut the thread when the task of this life was fulfilled. This description is for me an accurate description of the web that I observe, the cause of its existence and how it is created.

When I stared to understand this, I saw more clearly the connections between earth radiation and man. I saw how the actions of man created or attracted the snakes/demons, and how these demons created diseases and disasters in man. Such demons may also create disease in people that live close by or are attached to those who carry the demons. Thus, it has been observed over the ages that living or sleeping on 'earth radiation' may cause disease, and also that it is impossible to free yourself from the demons, unless you know how to do so (see later).

Demons can also be created through deeds of violence towards nature: If we kill weeds or insects with the help of chemicals (e.g. Roundup); if we slaughter a healthy cow or horse; if we cut down whole areas of forest with huge machines, then strong demons of disharmony will be created.

---

[*] Akasha (Sanskrit *ākāśa*, is a term for 'æther' in traditional Indian cosmology. The term was also adopted in Western occultism and spiritualism in the late nineteenth century. The Sanskrit word is derived from a root *kāś*, meaning 'to be visible'. The Western religious philosophy called Theosophy popularized the word Akasha as an adjective, through the use of the term 'Akashic records' or 'Akashic library', referring to an ethereal compendium of all knowledge and history.

[†] The term *Edda* ('ɛdə/; Old Norse *Edda*, plural *Eddur*) applies to the Old Norse *Edda* and has been adapted to fit the collection of poems known as the *Poetic Edda* which lacks an original title. Both works were written down in Iceland during the thirteenth century in Icelandic, although they contain material from earlier traditional sources, reaching into the Viking Age.

[‡] The *Norns* (Old Norse: *Norn*, plural: *Nornir*) in Norse mythology are female beings who rule the destiny of gods and men. They roughly correspond to other controllers of humans' destiny, the Fates, elsewhere in European mythology.

Summary

- All our actions conducted through passions such as greed, hate, jealousy and anger, create luciferic demons.
- All deeds done with the help of machines, cold thoughts, slaughterhouses or cutting down trees, create ahrimanic demons.
- All deeds that betray the truth, lead people astray or try to convert people to religions create azuric demons.

We may say that demons of a lower rank than humans, especially those of the three elemental regions, are created by man.

There are, as we now understand, many different kinds of earth radiation:

1. Electromagnetic radiation from the earth itself (radiation from the development of the earth).
2. Radiation from the nine (of twelve) layers of the earth (see page 84), mainly of ahrimanic influence.
3. Electromagnetic radiation created by human technology (high voltage pylons or mobile phones).
4. Spiritual radiation, from actions committed at the place where the radiation is found (usually called 'geopathic radiation'), caused mainly by ahrimanic demons. This has a huge influence in the creation of disease.
5. Spiritual radiation (both luciferic and ahrimanic demons) that follows the individual human being. This causes disease, mainly for the person in question.
6. Radiation from the cosmos (from higher beings of many kinds, among other demonic, angelic or planetary beings).

And so on ...

The obvious and detectable effects of earth radiation

Historical background

Knowledge of radiation from the earth and from aquifers (natural water lines in underground rock fissures) has a long tradition. One early reference is in the books of Moses. The story tells of the Israelites suffering from thirst in the desert. Moses took his stick and hit the rock and water gushed forth. The German expression *rotenschlägen* (to hit or beat something with a rod) refers to the European tradition of diviners using twigs or Y-sticks from hazel or other trees to locate water or metals underground.

There are many references of such events throughout history. It is mentioned in China that Emperor Kuanggu (2400 BC) made laws about how land that was used for building houses on should be examined beforehand in relation to geopathic radiation. Fengshui Yingli is the Chinese term for geopathic stress. It literally means wind and water stress. The Chinese system of Fengshui (literally, wind and water) includes an examination of the area for geopathic lines. These were called Dragon Paths (*Longlu*), or Dragon Channels / Vessels (*Longmai*). Where these lines/paths cross each other, the demons cooperate in strengthening the disease demons that abide in the body of the person that sleeps there.

Fengshui is still used today to position doors, windows, rooms, mirrors, beds, work areas, wind-chimes, etc. in the interiors of houses, shops, hotels, and so on. It aims to get the best flow of natural energy throughout the building and to banish, allay, or avoid geopathic or noxious earth energies where possible.

A—Twig. B—Trench.

Woodcut illustrating dowsers, by Georgius Agricolas, Basel 1556.

Several Native American cultures have the same rules. If a tent was to be put up or a camp built, one should first sit down and talk with the spirits about whether it was the right place or not. This practice can be found especially among the Hopi Indians in America. We find the same tradition in India, where it is of great importance to find the right place to put a bed. Several woodcarvings from fourteenth–sixteenth century show diviners (branch bearers) searching for earth radiation of various kinds.

The earth's electromagnetic fields ('physical' Earth radiation)

Referring to the research of the famous American Dr Becker, Bio-electrical Theory,[*] the essential conclusions (modified by me to fit the demonological explanations) are:

- The electromagnetic field of the earth itself is related to the cooperation (electric = ahrimanic, magnetic = luciferic) of both ahrimanic and luciferic demons that have become physical.
- Over millions of years, our biorhythms have developed in the earth's fluctuating electromagnetic fields (earth radiation) and are dependent on these fields. We are in fact dependent on the existence of both Ahriman and Lucifer to develop as human beings in full freedom.
- Illness occurs both when the physical earth radiation, especially man-made earth radiation, is too strong. Degenerative diseases will then develop when the ahrimanic demons are the strongest, and infectious diseases when the luciferic demons predominate.

Biorhythms

Biorhythms guide the body and the variations in our life processes (heart-process, lung-process, liver-process, menstruation cycle, etc.).

The life rhythms that we adopt (our usual patterns or set times for sleeping, eating and working, etc.) influence our bodily functions and energetic stamina, and vice versa.

Environmental earth radiation includes electric fields, radio, TV, laptops, computers, equipment that uses microwaves, high frequency radiation such as alpha, beta and gamma radiation, cosmic radiation and

---

[*]Bioelectrical Theory attempts to merge Eastern and Western ways of thinking. It explains the acupuncture effects from weak electrical currents, which penetrate to every part of the organism. Abnormalities in these currents can be of diagnostic value because the electrical conductivity of pathological parts of the body changes.

other types of geopathic radiation. All these forms of radiation affect us. We meet these influences in our everyday life as sound, light and other electromagnetic and spiritual radiation. Our five senses (sight, hearing, touch, taste and smell) normally do not perceive such forms of radiation, but our sixth sense, or dowsing, can sense them.

All these types of earth radiation interfere with each other. They create complicated patterns that influence the organs of the body, the processes and the biorhythms. Therefore, the influence varies from one individual to the next and from one place to another. That is why we cannot predict which person or animal will develop disorders, which places will manifest the disorders, or which specific disorders will arise. However, despite that, it is very important that we can diagnose the cause.

At this point, I must again insert my own demonological and spiritual-scientific considerations. Two of the most important factors in developing diseases from the influence of earth radiation are:

1. The strength and virulence of the demons behind the electric, magnetic or spiritual radiation present at any given site.
2. The vulnerability of the three auras that surround us: the etheric, the astral and the consciousness ('I') auras. Many people who are especially sensitive to earth radiation have 'holes' in their auras, through which the demonic influences may enter (and leave).

I have observed that almost all people who are hypersensitive to earth radiation have distinct holes in their auras. These must be 'closed' if they should have any chance of regaining normal health. This closure may be brought about mainly through understanding the cause of the hole, which may be a former trauma, misuse of drugs or immoral/wrong thought-forms, but it can also be done by physical means such as wrappings of wool or turf.

Example
A veterinary colleague working in Florida had many chronic problems with her knees, stomach and stamina. She had been to several very skilled therapists, but their treatments had made her worse. She flew to Norway to seek my help. I diagnosed that the cause of her problems was because the energy of her upper body was not flowing down to her lower body. When I told her this she said that the other therapists had diagnosed the same cause, but that their treatments had just made her worse.

Directing my spiritual vision at her knees, I clearly saw a hole there, through which energy leaked out. This hole was caused by (and held open by) a demon, created by her (my colleague's) mistreatment of the knees of a client's horse.

At that time, I did not know that the only lasting solution to such a problem was to ask the demon for forgiveness for my colleague's error, so I asked her to apply a layer of wool over the hole. This worked very well, but she had to wear the wrapping for one year before it was healed. However, her symptoms vanished immediately.

As Dr Becker concludes, it is important not to disturb normal earth radiation and magnetic fields and, in so far as is possible, to limit man-made and artificial fields, or excessive natural fields.

As far as possible, we should:

- Avoid strong artificial radiation from mobile telephones, high-voltage cables and transformers and electric equipment, etc.
- Avoid strong geopathic radiation, especially that which occurs over crossing aquifers or other strong geopathic radiation relating to earlier misdeeds carried out on that particular spot.

We should try to develop our ability to detect these stimuli (or get help from others to do so). We also should educate as many people as possible that these noxious effects exist.

Summarized below are some of the symptoms and effects that one may expect as a result of chronic exposure to excessive earth radiation or geopathic radiation, especially from crossing aquifers or from demonic forces related to human actions.

- If the ahrimanic forces get the upper hand, sclerotic and calcifying diseases will develop.
- If the luciferic forces get the upper hand, infections and fever will develop.
- If the azuric forces get the upper hand, mental disturbances of egoism and self-aggrandisement will prevail.

Today the ahrimanic forces are the strongest.[*] Some centuries ago, the luciferic forces were the strongest. In the future, the azuric forces will predominate.

Effects of geopathic radiation

Plants

Effects of geopathic stress on plants include twisted growth in trees and dead or stunted growth in avenues of trees. Fruit trees are most sensitive;

---

[*] Cancer is often caused by the ahrimanic demon overwhelming the luciferic demon. Therapies such as art therapy and the use of oil of cannabis will therefore stimulate the luciferic demon and restore a balance between the two forces, and can thus have a healing effect on cancer.

redwoods and ash are most resilient. Garden hedges can show the effects of geopathic radiation clearly: some of the hedge-shrubs die or become stunted. Affected shrubs have fewer and smaller leaves. Hedges do not look healthy.

The first reports of the effect of geopathic radiation on plants came from Germany in the late 1800s. Fruit trees, especially apple trees, try to avoid geopathic radiation by growing away from it. They become crooked, deformed and non-productive. The trunk may split in two and the branches that grow directly over the area of radiation become deformed. Cherry and sweet cherry trees have stunted development, malformed branches and cankers, such as we often see in birch trees.

Cankers or tumours on birch trees are quite common in areas of geopathic stress, where whole groups of birch trees, full of so-called 'crows nests', can be found. It is proven that viruses cause these tumours on trees but this does not explain why some trees are attacked and others not. It is the same in humans and animals; viruses and bacteria surround us but disease can manifest only under certain conditions. Stress weakens the immune system of plants and animals, thus allowing bacteria, viruses and fungal infections to thrive.

It is most important not to try to explain disease as due to viruses or bacteria per se, but rather by stress-induced immunosuppression, i.e., by a reduction of the host's resistance to these organisms. Immunosuppression occurs when we are exposed to excessive earth radiation over a long period of time, i.e., geopathic radiation, electric installations, TV or heating cables in the floor, etc.

Geopathic stress can cause lightning to strike trees. Like the flow of electricity, lightning bolts seek the paths of least resistance through the air. The exact places where they hit the ground are not random; they are places where electrical resistance is lowest, i.e., where conductivity is highest.

Trees that are struck by lightning usually are directly over, or very close to, geopathic lines. Oak trees like to grow near underground water, hence their attractiveness to lightning strikes. Elder trees thrive in damp places, especially on riverbanks, and are attracted to geopathic stress.

Animals

In my practice, I have found it almost impossible to treat animals or humans successfully if they remain exposed to a precipitating stressor, such as geopathic radiation. In contrast, my clinical results improve greatly if I can show the owner or subject how to escape from the stressor. Chronic stress and geopathic radiation decrease immunocompetence and weaken the immune system.

Animals that are free to roam at will seem to avoid areas of noxious radiation. This is the case with most domestic animals. However, animals often are forced to stay for prolonged periods in or over areas of adverse electromagnetic fields, or areas of geopathic radiation. This causes stress and disease, called geopathic stress. Animals that are chronically exposed to geopathic radiation are more vulnerable to infection, ketosis and infertility. They are less likely to thrive than those that are not exposed. However, cows on the point of calving often choose these zones in a field and lie down there to have their calves.

Animals that seek out radiation
Certain animals, such as owls, bats and cats, seek out areas of strong radiation for their dwelling places. Traditionally, these animals have been associated with darkness or evil powers (as spiritual radiation is related to karma, and karma is often considered evil). Also, other animals, such as ants, bees and wasps, show affinity to the earth's radiation. Bees that swarm often settle in trees that are growing over strong areas of radiation. Beehives placed over crossing aquifers produce more honey than hives placed away from those zones.

Ants' paths usually follow a dowsing reaction line, and we can often see the lines of radiation in how ants' paths lead out from the nest. Experiments were done to shield ants' nests from geopathic radiation and the result was that the ants left the nest the following year. They preferred not to stay for the winter in a nest that had no radiation (Rupert Sheldrake). A possible explanation is that a nest over a strong dowsing zone usually has underground water directly below it.[*]

I have often observed that people bitten by mosquitoes are bitten at the exact acupuncture-point that needs treatment, i.e. at the pathological point. For me, this all confirms the relationship of insects to the pathological ahrimanic earth radiation, associated diseases and the Eighth Sphere. Insects are attracted by disease, especially those of ahrimanic demons.

---

[*] Another explanation why insects are attracted to the demonic expression of spiritual or electromagnetic radiation may be that all the life forms in the Eighth Sphere are insect-like (see the Addendum on page 151 on the effects of different drugs).

What is the Eighth Sphere?

To understand this expression, we have to understand that the Eighth Sphere is not a particularly well-known realm or a greatly understood concept among people with spiritual interests. For those who know the concept it is quite frightening. It is the sphere where all ahrimanic deeds, thoughts and concepts materialize in a separate physical planet, which in the far future will be left behind by the common development of the universe and of human kind. It is where deeds done without soul or consciousness will end. It seems to me also to be a place where all our experiences with synthetic drugs, synthetic additives, pharmaceutical medicines or artificial food will take us. In addition, our work and pre-occupation within the field of computer technology—machines without soul—discussions on social media, conversations through emails and all lifeless computer interactions where the soul cannot enter, will end up in the Eighth Sphere. Many occultists have spoken and written about the Eighth Sphere, but there has been much disagreement and discussion about what it is, where it is and how it is organized. Some think it is connected to our present moon, whilst some believe it to be 'sub-earthly'.

Rudolf Steiner has given some lectures on this subject.[*] This is a summary of what he says. To present this correctly, the Eighth Sphere belongs to our physical earth. We are surrounded everywhere by 'Imaginations' into which mineral materiality is continually drawn. Its substance is far denser than the other mineralized substances. Its density is of a more physical-mineral character than exists anywhere on the earth. Hence, Lucifer and Ahriman cannot dissolve it away into their world of Imaginations. This sphere circles around us as a globe of dense matter, solid and indestructible.

Even if 'normal' animals avoid geopathic radiation lines, they often follow such lines for their pathways; or, as is seen in the more recent investigation carried out by dowsers, the geopathic lines are created just where people or animals travel. An older explanation for this is as follows: if we take into consideration that plant growth is diminished along these lines, it would be natural for animals to move around where it is easiest to pass. In this way, we cannot say that they follow the paths of radiation but, rather, they choose the path of least resistance.

---

[*] See *The Occult Movement in the Nineteenth Century*, lectures 4 & 5, Dornach, October 1915, GA 254; *Foundations of Esoterism*, lectures 14 & 18, Berlin, October 1905, GA 93a.

There is increasing evidence, however, that the geopathic radiation is created by the activities of humans themselves. For example, traditional dowsers believed that nearly all of the old church sites were built upon or were in strict relation to ley lines or other patterns of geopathic radiation. The same was also found in relation to old trails, roads, burial sites and places of worship. To investigate this, a group of Scandinavian dowsers, including myself, followed closely the development of all energetic patterns relating to newly-built churches and roads. We then discovered something amazing: the grid of radiation was organized and created as the construction proceeded. The area where a new church was to be built could be totally clean and free from earth radiation, but after the church was built, the radiation pattern usually seen in connection with ancient churches was present.

I once experienced something similar at a biodynamic farm in Vestfold, Norway. The farmer, Asbjørn Lavoll, was to make an investigation into the effect of different kinds of natural fertilizers. We found a 'clean' area, so that the different kinds of radiation should not interfere with the results. I stood there, watching as he proceeded with his investigations. However, as soon as the farmer lined up the different squares that were to be used in the trial, a strong pattern of radiation appeared. This radiation was related to the planet Saturn and to the metal lead. Such patterns are often seen when a materialistic way of thinking excludes a more spiritual way of thinking. The intention of the farmer to make rectangular squares in which he was to compare the effect of different spiritually-prepared fertilizers expressed itself as an ahrimanic grid of spiritual power, drawing its force from Saturn.

These findings are very similar to the modern results within quantum-physical investigations, where the outcomes of the investigations are highly influenced by the minds of the researchers. This indicates that the human mind is the primary source of these ley lines and other spiritual radiation, commonly called geo-pathological influence.

Humans

As is the case with animals, excessive or qualitatively negative earth radiation (geopathic radiation or other fields) affect humans adversely. The dowsing literature in many countries has a litany of hundreds of disorders that geopathic or noxious earth radiation can induce. These include insomnia, neurasthenia, depression, sudden death syndrome in babies, asthma, arthralgia, arthritis, cancer, degenerative diseases such as multiple sclerosis, etc. I have seen many examples of this in my practice.

Examples

- *Children who cry and cry for months, immediately stop crying once their beds are moved 0.5 metres away from where they originally stood.*
- *Older people with chronic ulcers and infections heal quickly after their beds are moved to another place.*
- *An old man had a small splinter in his finger and the wound became infected. He was not concerned about the infection, but when the finger became swollen, he went to the doctor. He was given antibiotics, but the infection did not cease. They had to amputate the finger. In this case, the surgeon tried to amputate as little as possible, with the result that the infection went into the hand. The hand was then amputated, but the infection went up into the arm. The lower arm was amputated, followed later by the upper arm. However, the infection went further up into the face, and when he came to my office, he was without his right arm and with his head looking like a cauliflower. The situation was terrible. I found that he was under a strong influence from a place-bound local demon (geopathic radiation), and he himself was very weakened in his right upper etheric and astral auras. I strengthened the auras and ordered the man to move away from the place where he was sleeping. The disease had gone on for several months, but already the next morning the infection was retreating, and after a few weeks the infection was gone. The local demon looked very much like the demon of the special bacteria that he had caught, so it was a case of triple bad luck that had brought about this unfortunate development.*

Cancer in humans chronically exposed to strong electrical fields

The National Cancer Institute, USA, stated on 27 May 2016:

> Many studies and scientific reviews have evaluated possible associations between exposure to non-ionizing EMFs and risk of cancer in children. Most of the research was on leukaemia and brain tumours, the two most common cancers in children. Studies have examined the correlation of these cancers with the vicinity of power lines, with magnetic fields in the home, and with exposure of parents to high levels of magnetic fields in the workplace. No consistent evidence for an association between any source of non-ionizing EMF and cancer has been found.

That statement must be viewed with great scepticism. No government will admit that EMFs, especially those caused by power lines, can cause cancer. This is because modern industry depends totally on electric power. Without electric power, mass unemployment, social unrest and anarchy would destroy the economies and social cohesion of modern societies.

Brain tumours and exposure to electrical fields

A colleague in Ireland emailed:

> Some years ago, the death rate from cancer in workers in a large national research institute was noted to be far above that in the general population. The institute had several laboratories in different parts of Ireland. An investigation was conducted to determine if the deaths could be work-related. The team included a medical doctor who specialized in environmental medicine and Trade Union representatives from each of the labs involved. I was one of the investigators.
>
> Exposure to lab reagents, gases, chemicals, carcinogens, nuclear materials etc. was examined. We could not find a satisfactory reason to explain the abnormal death rate. In one lab, two genetically unrelated scientists had died within a short interval of each other. The cause of death in both cases was a rare brain tumour. Both men worked in adjoining offices. The fuse box for the lab's power supply was just outside the wall of one office and multiple power cables from that fuse box ran directly over the heads of both men. The doctor discounted any causality between the cancer in both men and exposure to an electrical field from the cables over their heads. Though I am an experienced researcher and veterinary clinician, not qualified in human medicine, I disagree with his medical verdict. I am convinced that my colleagues died from cancer, triggered by EMFs emitted by the power cables.

Energy production and demons

Norwegian folklore tells how elementals can be changed into demons. Before 1900, most families in Norway believed in the existence of the elementals, known as *Nisse*, *Dverger* and *Hulder* among others. It was also believed that if humans did not treat the elementals properly and with respect, the elementals could turn into malevolent entities such as demons. In this state, they could harm humans or animals. Therefore, many farmers put out food for the elementals, especially around Christmas time.

In the book *Lord of the Rings*, the character Saruman describes how the Orchs (demons) came into existence. To paraphrase, the Orchs were once elves; good and benevolent beings. They were then seized by evil forces, by the greed and power-hunger of men, and that changed them into malevolent beings. These malevolent beings can be changed into beings of even greater malevolence with the help of black magic.

Energy production and demons

When humans produce artificial energy derived from many new sources (electricity, nuclear energy, wind turbines, solar energy), benevolent elementals are changed into demons, or new demons are created. An example of this is that elementals within the wind are caught by the wind turbines, and then they are changed by the nature of the technology to demonic ahrimanic elementals.

When 'old' sources of energy are used, such as burning of wood, coals and oils, there are a large number of elementals present called 'salamanders'. These are not changed into malevolent elementals. This happens only when magnetism, electricity or nuclear power is the source of the energy.

Fire, Air, Earth and Water are the four basic elements of nature. Within each of the four elements, there are three realms or levels of elemental beings. All the elemental beings of all three realms together form the spiritual essence of that element. The elementals are made up of etheric substance that is unique and specific to that particular element.

The beings of the third realm are often called 'nature spirits'. These beings are living entities, often resembling humans in shape but inhabiting a world of their own. The elemental beings in the elemental kingdoms work primarily on the mental plane and are known as 'builders of form'. Their speciality is to translate 'thought forms' into physical forms by transforming spiritual patterns initially into astral patterns, then into etheric patterns and finally physical patterns. Each of them is a specialist in creating some specific form, whether it is an electron or interstellar space.

Elementals range in size from smaller than an electron to vaster than galactic space. Like the angels, elemental beings begin their evolution as small in size and increase as they evolve. The elementals serving on the planet Earth materialize whatever they pick up from the thoughts and feelings of mankind. This relationship was intended to facilitate the re-manifestation of 'heaven on earth'. They do not remain individualized like humans. They may be etheric thought forms, yet they have etheric flesh, blood and bones. They live, eat, talk, act and sleep. They cannot be destroyed by material elements such as Fire, Air, Earth and Water because they are etheric in nature. They are not immortal. When their work is finished they are absorbed back into the ocean of spirit. They live a very long time—300 to 1,000 years and have the power to change their size and appearance at will. However, they cannot change elements.

Earth—gnomes

The nature spirits of the earth are called gnomes. There are many sub-groups: brownies, dryads, durdalis, earth spirits, elves, hamadryads, pans, pygmies, sylvestres, satyrs, nisser, dverger, hulder and many more.

Billions of elemental beings from the first, second and third realm tend the earth through the cycles of the four seasons and see to it that all living things are supplied with their daily needs. They also process the waste and by-products that are an inevitable part of our everyday existence and purge the earth of poisons and pollutants that are dangerous to the physical bodies of man, animal and plant life, including toxic wastes, industrial effluvia, pesticides, acid rain, nuclear radiation and every abuse of the earth.

On a spiritual level, the gnomes have an even graver duty. They must clean up the imprints of man's discord and negativity that remain at energetic levels in the earth. War, murder, rape, child abuse, the senseless killing and torture of animals, profit seeking at the expense of the environment as well as hatred, anger, discord, gossip—all these create an accumulation of negatively charged energy that creates demonic elementals (earth radiation) and becomes a heavy weight on the earth body and on the beneficial nature spirits.

Fire—salamanders

The salamanders are the spirits of Fire. Without these beings, fire cannot exist. You cannot light a match without a salamander being present. There are many families of salamanders, differing in size, appearance and dignity. Some people have seen them as small balls of light, but most commonly they are perceived as being lizard-like in shape and about a foot or more in length. The salamanders are considered the strongest and most powerful of all the elementals. Salamanders have the ability to extend their size or diminish it, as needed. If you ever need to light a campfire in the wilderness, call to the salamanders and they will help you.

It is said that salamanders (and other elemental beings) can be mischievous, even malicious at times. For example, a fiery temper and inharmonious conditions in a person's home can cause these beings to make trouble. They are like children in that they don't fully understand the results of their actions. They are greatly affected by human thinking, as are all nature spirits.

Air—sylphs

Sylphs are Air elementals. Their element has the highest vibratory rate of the four. They live to be hundreds of years old, often reaching one thousand without appearing old. They are said to live on the tops of mountains. Sylphs often assume human form but only for short periods of time. They vary in size, from as large as a human to something much smaller. They are volatile and changeable. The winds are their particular vehicle. They work through the gases and ethers of the earth and are kind towards humans. They are usually seen with wings, looking like cherubs or fairies. Because of their connection to air, which is associated with the spiritual aspect, one of their functions is to help humans receive inspiration. The sylphs are drawn to those who use their minds, particularly those involved with the creative arts.

Water—undines

Undines are the elemental beings that live in Water. They are able to control, to a great degree, the course and function of the Water element. Etheric in nature, they exist within water itself and this is why they cannot be seen with normal, physical, vision. These beings are beautiful to look at and are very graceful. They are often seen riding the waves of the ocean. They can also be found in rocky pools and in marshlands. They are clothed in shimmering substances resembling water but shining with all the colours of the sea, predominantly green. The concept of the mermaid is connected with these elemental beings. The undines also work with the plants that grow under the water and with the motion of water. Some undines inhabit waterfalls; others live in rivers and lakes. Every fountain has its nymph. Every ocean has its oceanids. The undines closely resemble humans in appearance and size, except for those inhabiting smaller streams and ponds. They often live in coral caves under the ocean or on the shores of lakes or the banks of rivers. Smaller undines live under lily pads.

The undines work with the vital essences and liquids of plants, animals and human beings. They are present in everything containing water. There are many families of undines. They are emotional beings, very friendly and open to being of service to humans. The smaller undines are often seen as winged beings that some people have mistakenly called fairies. Those winged beings are seen near flowers that grow in watery areas. The subgroups are: limoniades, mermaids, naiads, oceanids, oreads, potamides, seamaids and water spirits.

As stated earlier, elementals are the spiritual foundation of nature and are also created by positive human deeds as well as ill ones. When electricity was created, man started to use this material energy source, created by the vibrations of atoms. This resulted in the creation of a lot of demonic elementals, or elementals on the verge of becoming demons.

This was difficult for me to understand until I visited the Amish community in New York state in 2015. One of the peculiarities about the Amish people is that they do not use electricity. Before I visited them, I thought that elementals were always serious, unsmiling and uninterested in humans, but when I came to the Amish community I was greeted by smiling elementals that were interested in me. I was deeply shaken by this observation and came to understand the terrible effect that electricity has on the world's elementals.

Rudolf Steiner has described the connection of different energy sources in relation to the elemental/demonic realms:

- Electricity creates ahrimanic elementals of demonic tendency.
- Magnetism creates luciferic elementals of demonic tendency.
- Nuclear power creates azuric elementals of demonic tendency.

In this connection, it is very interesting to observe how electricity and magnetism is used in the healing of different diseases in humans and animals. Magnets sometimes work wonders, as in the cases of rheumatism and related ailments, and sometimes not. Electric therapeutic currents sometimes work wonders, and again sometimes not.

The answer to this riddle is the cooperation of ahrimanic and luciferic demons in the creation and development of disease.

As described later in this book, the cooperation of ahrimanic and luciferic demons in the creation and development of disease holds the answer to this riddle. This is because magnetism summons luciferic demons whereas electricity summons ahrimanic demons. Thus, magnetic devices can cure symptoms caused by ahrimanic demons, because luciferic demons counteract the effects of ahrimanic demons. Similarly, electric devices can cure symptoms caused by luciferic demons because ahrimanic demons counteract the effects of luciferic demons.

This is also why marijuana is reported to be beneficial in many diseases but may totally fail to help in others. It even works differently on the same symptoms in different people. This is because marijuana strengthens the luciferic demons, much like magnetism, and this may counteract the ahrimanic symptoms.

I emphasize that treating the Middle Point with Christ Consciousness counteracts both luciferic and ahrimanic demons simultaneously.

I noted an interesting phenomenon on two occasions: Christ Consciousness may heal drug addicts or alcoholics in seconds. Addicts treated via the Middle Point with Christ Consciousness do not need drugs to counteract either ahrimanic or luciferic demons. The Addendum (see page 151) discusses the subject of drug use and addiction in more detail.

I will also add here some information from a North American Indian who was interviewed by a journalist. He said: '. . . after we got electricity here in the camp, we do not hear the spirits of nature speaking to us anymore'.

Rudolf Steiner on disease and the doppelgänger, and demons of ahrimanic and luciferic nature and their relation to Earth radiation

The following quotes are from a lecture that Rudolf Steiner held in St Gallen on 16 November 1917.* At first, he describes how the spiritual world and the physical world are closely connected. He then goes on:

> We human beings consist of body, soul, and spirit, but that is by no means an exhaustive statement concerning our being. Our body, our soul, our spirit, are what first approach our consciousness, as it were, but they are not everything standing in connection with our existence. Not in the least! What I am about to say is connected with certain mysteries of human becoming, of human nature, which must be known today and become ever better known. [. . .] The opportunity therefore exists a short time before we are born for another spiritual being in addition to our soul to take possession of our body, of the subconscious part of our body.

Then Rudolf Steiner describes the mysterious ahrimanic doppelgänger.

> A short time before we are born we are permeated by another being; in our terminology we would call it an ahrimanic spirit-being. This is within us just as our own soul is within us. These beings spend their life using human beings in order to be able to be in the sphere where they want to be. These beings have an extraordinarily high intelligence and a significantly developed will, but no warmth of heart at all, nothing of what we call human soul warmth (*Gemüt*). Thus, we go through life in such a way that we have both our souls and a doppelgänger of this kind, who is much cleverer, very much cleverer than we are; who is very intelligent, but with a Mephistophelian intelligence, an ahrimanic intelligence, and also an ahrimanic will, a very strong will, a will that is

---

* The full lectures are published in *Secret Brotherhoods and the Mystery of the Human Double*, Rudolf Steiner Press 2004.

much more akin to the nature-forces than our human will, which is regulated by the warmth of soul.

In the nineteenth century, natural science discovered that the nervous system is permeated by electrical forces, which of course is right. When natural scientists believe that the nerve-force that belongs to us as the basis of our conceptual life has something to do with electrical streams that go through our nerves, they are incorrect. For the electrical streams, which are the forces put into us by the being I have just mentioned and described, do not belong to our own being at all. We carry electrical streams in us, but they are of a purely ahrimanic nature. These beings are of high intelligence, of pure Mephistophelian intelligence, and with a will more akin to nature than can be said of the human will. These beings once decided out of their own will that they did not want to live in that world in which they were destined to live by the wisdom-filled gods of the higher hierarchies. They wanted to conquer the earth, and to do this they needed bodies; they did not have bodies of their own. They make use of the human body as much as they can, because the human soul cannot entirely fill up the human body. These beings are able to enter human bodies at a definite time before the human being is born, and below the threshold of our consciousness, they accompany us. There is only one thing in human life that they absolutely cannot endure: they cannot endure death. Therefore, they must always leave the human body in which they have established themselves, before that body succumbs to death. This is a very harsh disappointment again and again, for just what they want to attain— to remain in human bodies beyond death—is thwarted. To do this would be a lofty achievement in the kingdom of these beings. Up until now, they have not attained it.

Then Rudolf Steiner describes the importance of the Christ, the Christ Consciousness, and what, as we will see later, creates the possibility of the Middle Point, of treating the diseases of ahrimanic origin without just translocating them.

Had the Mystery of Golgotha not occurred, had Christ not passed through the Mystery of Golgotha, conditions on Earth would have been such that these beings would long ago have attained the possibility of remaining within the human being when he is karmically predestined for death. Then they would have completely triumphed over human evolution on Earth, they would have become masters of human evolution on Earth. It is of tremendous and profound significance to have insight into the connection between Christ passing through the Mystery of Golgotha and these beings that want to conquer death in human nature but are not yet able today to endure it. They must always avoid experiencing in the human body the hour when the human being is predestined to die. They must avoid maintaining his body beyond the hour of death, of prolonging the life of his body beyond the hour of death.

Then Rudolf Steiner describes the occult brotherhoods that use this knowledge for their own benefit:

This matter of which I am now speaking has long been known to certain occult brotherhoods. They knew these things well and withheld them from humanity (again, we do not want to discuss their right to do so). Today, conditions are such that it is impossible not to equip people gradually with such concepts, which they will need when they have passed through the portal of death. Everything that the human being experiences here, even what he experiences below the threshold of consciousness, he needs after death, because he must look back upon this life, and in looking back this life must be entirely comprehensible. The worst thing is for him to be unable to do this. An individual will not have sufficient concepts to understand this life on looking back at it, if he cannot shed light on a being that takes over a portion of our life. This is an ahrimanic being, which takes possession of us before our birth and always remains with us, always creating a figure around us in our subconscious. This will be the case unless we can repeatedly shed light upon it. For wisdom becomes light after death. These beings are in general very important for human life, and knowledge of them must gradually lay hold of the human being. Only it must lay hold of human beings in the right way. It must not be disseminated to humanity only by those occult brotherhoods who make it a power issue, intending thereby to enhance their own power. Above all, it must not be guarded further for the sake of enhancing the power of certain egotistically-minded brotherhoods. Humanity strives for universal knowledge, and that knowledge must be disseminated. In the future it will no longer be wholesome for occult brotherhoods to be able to employ such things for the extension of their power. In the coming centuries, human beings must increasingly gain knowledge of the doppelgänger. The human being in the coming centuries will have to know more and more that he bears such a doppelgänger within him, such an ahrimanic-Mephistophelian one. The human being must know this. Today the human being is already developing a great many concepts, but they are actually obscured, because the human being does not yet know how to deal with them in the right way. The human being develops concepts today that can have a proper basis only when they are brought together with the facts that lie at their foundation.

Then Rudolf Steiner lectures about the connection of the doppelgänger, ahrimanic entities and disease:

And here something is disclosed that in the future must be followed up if the human race is not to experience endless hindrances and endless horrors. This doppelgänger about which I have spoken is nothing more or less than the creator of all physical illnesses that emerge spontaneously from within; and to know him fully is the basis of holistic medicine. He is the creator of all illnesses that emerge spontaneously from within, and a brother of his, who is luciferic, is the creator of all neurasthenic, neurotic and hysterical illnesses. Thus, medicine must become spiritual in two directions. The demand for this is shown by the intrusion of views such as those of psychoanalysis and the like, where one keeps house with spiritual entities, as it were, but with inadequate means of knowledge so that one can do nothing at all with the phenomena that will intrude more and more into human life. For certain things need to happen, things that may even be harmful in a certain direction, because the human being must be exposed to what is harmful in order to overcome it and thereby gain strength.

As I have said, this ahrimanic doppelgänger is really the creator of all illnesses that have an organ-based foundation that are not merely functional. In order to understand this fully, however, one must know a great deal more. One must know, for example, that our entire earth is not the dead product that mineralogy or geology thinks it to be, but is a living being. Geology knows as much of the earth as we would know about the human being if we knew only of the skeletal system. Imagine that you were unable to perceive other people with usual sense perception and instead there were only x-rays of our fellow human beings. Then you would know only the skeletal system of your acquaintances. You would know as much about the human being as the geologists and science in general know about the earth. Imagine coming to this lecture and seeing all of the respected ladies and gentlemen you find here as nothing more than bones. Then you would have as much consciousness of the people present here as science has of the earth.

[...] When the human being entered into this epoch, the guiding spiritual beings had to consider his special weakness in relation to the doppelgänger. Had the human being taken into his consciousness the knowledge of the doppelgänger, it would have gone badly. Before the fourteenth century, the human being had to be protected, so that he would take in very little of what was suggestive in any way of the doppelgänger. Therefore, the knowledge of this doppelgänger that existed throughout earlier ages was lost. Humanity had to be guarded so that it would not take up anything of the theory of this doppelgänger; not only this, however, but it had to come in contact with as little as possible of anything connected with this doppelgänger.

Then Rudolf Steiner described the relation of the doppelgänger (and all ahrimanic beings) to geography:

[...] Since the ninth or tenth century, conditions in Europe were gradually adjusted in such a way that they lost the connection to America, a connection that was still important for human beings in earlier centuries, the sixth and seventh centuries AD. Beginning in the ninth century and especially from the twelfth century, the entire shipping exchange with America was abolished. This may sound very strange to you. You will say, 'We have never heard anything like this in history.' In many respects, history is just a *fable convenue*, a legend; for in earlier centuries ships continually sailed from Norway to America. Of course, it was not called America, it had a different name at that time. America was known to be the region where the magnetic forces particularly arose that brought the human being into relation with the doppelgänger. For the clearest relations to the doppelgänger proceed from that region of the earth that comprises the American continent. In earlier centuries, people sailed to America in Norwegian ships and studied illnesses there. The illnesses in America brought about under the influence of earthly magnetism were studied, and the mysterious origin of the older European shamanic medicine is to be sought there. In America, one could observe the course of illness that could not have been observed in Europe, where people were more sensitive with regard to the influence of the doppelgänger. It then became necessary for the connection with America to be gradually forgotten, and this was essentially brought about through the edicts of the Roman Catholic Church.

Only after the beginning of the fifth post-Atlantean epoch was America 'rediscovered'. This was only a rediscovery, however, which is so significant because the powers that were at work actually achieved their purpose: that little would be reported in the record of the ancient relations between Europe and America. Europe had to be protected from the influence of the Western world. This is the significant historical arrangement that was cultivated by wisdom-filled world powers. Europe had to be protected for a long time from all these influences; and it could not have been protected if the European world had not been completely shut off from America in the times before the fifteenth century.

Medicine can endure only if it is a spiritual science, for illnesses come from a spiritual being that only makes use of the human body in order to profit from it, which it cannot do in the place assigned to it by the wise guidance of the world, against which it has revolted, as I have shown you. This is actually an ahrimanic-Mephistophelian being within human nature, which before birth is inhaled into the human body and leaves this human body only because it cannot endure death under its present conditions. Illnesses emerge because this being works in the human being. Moreover, when remedies are employed, it means that something is given to this being from the outer world that it otherwise seeks through the human being. If I provide a remedy for the human body when this ahrimanic-Mephistophelean being is at work, I give it something else. I stroke this being, as it were. I come to terms with it, so that it lets go of the human being and becomes satisfied with what I have tossed into its jaws as a remedy.

Christ, demons (luciferic, azuric and ahrimanic), the Eighth Sphere and Quantum Physics

Can quantum physics solve the problem or riddle of dark energy?

Today, the connection between Christ, demons (luciferic, azuric and ahrimanic), the Eighth Sphere and quantum physics, is of utmost interest and importance. Albert Einstein had a deep feeling or intuition about this when he said that God does not play dice. He felt that quantum physics brought in something that was opposed to God.

What do particles that come into existence out of a vacuum (i.e. from a non-material existence), bring into this world? Where do they come from?

Paul Emberson, in his three-volume work *From Gondishapur to Silicon Valley*, has elaborated on this question. His conclusions are that our work with, and use of, elemental particles and quantum physics, may be a direct opening between our world, the demonic azuric world and the Eighth Sphere.

How can we say that quantum physics is an opening to the spiritual world and in particular an opening to the world of the adversaries? Some of the discoveries made within quantum physics are spiritual in substance:

1. Entanglement; that particles of the same origin are forever connected. This is a spiritual law, not a law of the physical world.
2. Non-locality; that a particle may be everywhere and nowhere, until
   it shows up. This is also one of the fundamental laws of the spiritual
   world. Some scientists even express this phenomenon as follows:
   that the elemental particles actually avoid the onlooker as soon as
   the onlooker can see the particle.
3. The entanglement between particles is immediate, time is of no
   importance. This is also a law of the spiritual world.

This shows that in quantum physics we are dealing with an area between
the physical world and the spiritual world. It also explains the problems I
got in treating cancer after being able to 'see' the demonic elementals
involved in the development of cancer. Also, with this insight, the
controversies between Niels Bohr and Albert Einstein disappear. The
issue is that we have not yet accepted the laws of the spiritual world.
Furthermore, what materializes from the spiritual world into the physical
world is probably connected to the world of the adversaries.

If we use LED light, quantum computers and other quantum-physical
inventions, then we open ourselves up to the azuric world, just as when
we use electricity we open to the ahrimanic world and when we use
magnetism we open to the luciferic world.

Some principles and problems within quantum physics are more easily
understood through spiritual science. The following six principles within
physics can say much about the observations of elementals and demons.

The six principles are:

1. The speed of light (constant in all directions).
2. The equivalence principle (within gravity).
3. The cosmological principle (that the cosmos is the same in all
   directions).
4. Quantization (all things are divided in small quantities or packages).
5. Uncertainty (before we see an elemental we don't know how or
   where it is).
6. Wave/particle duality (all things are both particle or wave).

Quantization says that everything consists of minimal packages. They are
elementals of the first level. Uncertainty principle says that the better you
'see' the elemental particle (being), the less you can predict where it goes.
(Actually, some say that the more you see the elemental the more it can
and will avoid you. I experienced just this in my cancer therapy, when the
cancer started to avoid me. That happened when I started to 'see' the

cancer elementals.) Entanglement is also explained by the elemental spiritual view. The elementals are together in the spiritual world and, as such, forever connected. There the time and distance are non-existent; also, the speed of light is not a restriction. The restriction is the border between the physical and the spiritual world.

Dark Energy

I have often observed that the demonic world—the world of the hordes of ahrimanic and luciferic beings—has a certain physical effect on the material world. We have seen this in the making of crop circles, as well as in the activity of poltergeists. We have also seen that the laws found in quantum physics are effects from the spiritual world. One effect I have seen is that the spirit world has a certain pull on the physical and material world. Can this pull explain the missing gravity or 'mass' that scientists are looking for to explain the behaviour of the cosmos?

The deeper layers of the body and the Earth. The origin of the radiation that feeds the demons, the ahrimanic beings and the doppelgänger

As background to this section, I refer briefly to my investigations of the layers of the human body. When making a pulse diagnosis, there are twelve layers through which we must penetrate between the skin and the centre of the heart. Most of my students stop at the fifth, sixth, seventh or eighth layer, and do not enter the heart. We need a little power to enter the heart, a little bravery, a little push.

The twelve layers of the body are as follows:

- The outer layers (first and second) relate to the astral body.
- The third and fourth layers relate to the material body: the third being our own physical, material body, and the fourth, the parasitic material body.
- The fifth to the eighth layers relate to the etheric body (the four ethers); the eighth touching the pericardium and the ninth touching the endocardium, where we encounter most hindrances in therapy.
- The inner layers (ninth to twelfth) are within the heart and relate to the 'I': the lower 'I' to the ninth, the middle 'I' to the tenth, the higher 'I' to the eleventh and the cosmic 'I', the Christ Consciousness, to the twelfth, where we are in the middle of the heart, the lamb (ram). We may also consider the layers within the heart as the future possibilities of human spiritual development, especially relating to the feminine part of the higher 'I's. These layers also

relate to the future development of the deeper layers of the earth itself, which today are evil but, in the future, can be transformed to good through the union of the Divine Mother and the Divine Father.

When we are in the centre of the heart, we might have the Imagination of standing at a cross. Actually, this cross is more than an Imagination: it is made out of true spiritual substance.

On the way through the twelve layers we may diagnose, experience and/or treat the different aspects present in these layers concerning diseases or spiritual realities.

What Rudolf Steiner says about the radiation or influence from the deeper layers of the Earth

The Earth consists of nine layers (according to Rudolf Steiner):

1. Mineral Earth, where we live.
2. Fluid Earth. Due to high-pressure, the materials here are fluid. This layer wants to expand through the first layer, to be released into the cosmos.
3. Damp (or Air) Earth. Here the substances are in a damp state and this layer is full of life. This layer wants to expand even more than the second layer. It is in close connection to human passions and the animal world and is filled with living streams consisting of animalistic and strong passions, such as we may observe in animals (hunger, greed, violence, the desire to kill and despair).
4. Watery Earth. Here all substances are in an astral form. The astral form is seen as the negative of the material form (like an old-fashioned negative photograph).
5. Fruit Earth is pure life. Everything is alive here.

Layers three, four and five are filled with life—etheric life—just like layers five to eight in the body.

6. Fire Earth. This is also in direct contact with human emotions, especially 'fiery' emotions. Human suffering will upset this layer and lead to volcanic activity. 'Dragon-Energies' can be found here (*Balrog Energy* as described in *The Lord of the Rings*). Fire Earth is related to the magnetic field of the Earth, and as such is related to Lucifer and earthquakes. It is here that volcanoes have their origin, connected to the uncontrolled emotions of man, especially greed and hate.

7. Mirroring Earth. Here man's uncontrolled ego can be nurtured. It is also called the Reflecting Earth. All the natural forces and laws are found here, but in their opposite form. All moral impulses are changed into their opposites. All colours appear in their opposite or complementary colour.

8. Splintering Earth (the layer where all numbers have their origin, according to Pythagoras). All living entities are here splintered into multiple 'copies' of their original. This layer is also the source of black magic. All good qualities are transformed into the opposite (as in the seventh layer). The eighth layer is the origin of all evil in the world.

9. Earth's Core, where the utmost evil can be found. Here is the deepest origin of black magic. This layer resembles both the human brain and the human heart. It contains both the demonic 'I', the lower 'I' as well as possibilities for the higher 'I's.

These four layers, the sixth, seventh, eighth and ninth, are the most evil parts of the earth. The ninth level is of great interest in these connections. In the body, this is where in a way we leave the physical earth and enter the spiritual realm (the four levels of the 'I', levels nine to twelve). The ninth level is actually not part of the earth, but part of the cosmos. However, the ninth level represents the lower 'I', and as such, this layer is also part of the evil layers, six to nine.

According to my own investigations, there are three more layers of the internal earth. These three layers, together with the ninth layer, resemble the internal heart of the human being. In the heart of the human being we find the possibility to develop the higher self, the cosmic consciousness and the Christ Consciousness. Here, there is also the possibility of a reunion between the Divine Mother and the Divine Father. So far, this has not yet developed, so the three last layers are more like possibilities for the future.

The seeds of these three layers were put there by Christ himself on the 4 April, in the year following the crucifixion at Golgotha, after which he descended through the earth, through all the various layers. Reaching the ninth layer, the ultimate evil, he placed the seeds of a future heart, a heart to be created by the actions of the human race, in correlation with the creation of the three higher selves in the heart of the human being:

Tenth: the layer of the human 'I' as a possibility for the future world.
Eleventh: the layer of the human higher 'I' as a possibility for the future world.
Twelfth: the layer of Christ Consciousness, the Christ 'I' as a possibility for the future world.

Demonic powers influence us, especially from the sixth and the ninth layer, and vice versa. If we are overpowered by greed and hate, the Fire Earth will rebel in volcanic eruptions and/or quakes. These influencing powers can only be counteracted through the strength of our higher 'I' and are in many ways equal to the effect of the higher 'I' on earth radiation. Both of these kinds of influences or radiations enter through our feet. To avoid this, we must 'wash our feet in Christ', which is the deeper meaning of the symbolic washing of the feet.

These twelve layers resemble the twelve layers of the body itself, as described in my book, *Sevenfold Way to Therapy*.

In the table below, I summarize the twelve layers of the body in brief (according to my own research) and relate them to the nine layers of the earth (as researched by Rudolf Steiner) and the additional three layers I have spoken of above, and the influences of the demonic realms.

	The layers of the body	**The layers of the earth**
1st layer	The astral sheath of the body	The physical Earth
2nd layer	The astral and the physical/material body	Fluid earth, high pressure, expansion
3rd layer	The physical/material body	Damp (or Air) Earth
4th layer	The parasitic bodies within our physical/material body and alien physical bodies (bacteria) that we use to digest foodstuffs	Water Earth or Form-Earth
5th layer	The etheric body I, warmth-ether (infrared). Also, the scars of the body, both physical and mental that have come from life's experiences of living in warmth	Fruit Earth
6th layer	The etheric body II, light-ether (blue = Ahriman, red = Lucifer). Also, the scars of the body, both physical and mental that have come from life, from living in light	Fire Earth
7th layer	The etheric body III, chemical ether (ultraviolet). Also, the scars of the body, both physical and mental that have come from life, from living in sounds and/or substances	Mirroring Earth or reflecting earth

8th layer	The etheric body IV (green). Also, the scars of the body, both physical and mental that have come from life, from living in life forces	Splintering Earth
9th layer	The demonic 'I', the lower 'I'. The lower passions that we are aware of. Ill will.	The core of the Earth
10th layer	The 'I', the Ego, egoism. The 'normal' self.	The 'I', the Ego, egoism, which may be transformed through the development of man into a good form of the 'I'
11th layer	The higher 'I', idealism. What we call the super-ego	The higher 'I', idealism, which may be transformed through the development of man into a good form of the 'I'
12th layer	The Christ 'I', the Divine Consciousness, Christ-Consciousness	The Christ 'I', the divine Consciousness, Christ-Consciousness, that may be transformed through the development of man into a good and angelic form of the 'I' (which may lift humans to the 10th hierarchy of angels)

The most interesting part of this comparison is the eighth layer of both the Earth and the body. In the Earth, this is the centre of evil, where Ahriman resides. The sixth and the eighth layers, especially, contain the evil forces. Rudolf Steiner describes the ninth layer as the core of the Earth. This core is like the human heart, in as far as the heart itself houses egoistic feelings. As the heart is the hope of humanity, the growing power of our higher selves resides there, and will in the future become the tenth, eleventh and twelfth layers, expressing Christ Consciousness and as such splitting off from the eighth layer (which will be in close connection, although not identical with, the Eighth Sphere). This Eighth Sphere will in the future branch off, as the material Earth will no longer be able to develop with the rest of the spiritualizing Earth and ascending humanity.

In the body, this is also the centre of evil, where the hindrances to therapy are to be found, where old scars are situated and where psychic traumas are remembered. Most interesting of all is the distance between the eighth and ninth layer. I used this distance for several years to diagnose so-called 'toxic scars': physical and psychological scars that hinder all kinds of treatment. In the seventh layer, the scars were present, but in the ninth layer, they were gone. Therefore, when there was no deficiency in the seventh layer, and a clear deficiency in the ninth layer, the conclusion was that there existed a toxic scar in the process, which showed deficiency in the seventh layer.

I used this difference to *find* the scars but did not realize at that time that it was possible to *treat* them from the twelfth layer. When we treat from the twelfth layer, the scars do not matter as they are of no significance. In the past, I only diagnosed my patients from the sixth to ninth layer, and then injected the physical scars with procaine, as described in Neural Therapy by Dr Ferdinand Hünecke.[*] Today I know that if I go to the twelfth layer, which I now always go directly to, *all* forms of scar treatment is unnecessary. This indicates that if we enter into Christ Consciousness, all old obstacles disappear.

In the context of this book, we could say: the old demons that hinder the progress of mankind are to be found in the eighth layer, but if we enter the Christ Consciousness of the twelfth layer, all the demons are dissolved.

The 'spiritual Ahrimanic radiation' from the deeper layers of the Earth enters both into the weakened organs or organic processes, but also through the weakened astral sheaths that surround and protect our body.

The auras

We have three main auras, the etheric, the astral and the spiritual 'I'-aura.

- The ahrimanic demons can enter mainly through the etheric aura.
- The luciferic demons can enter mainly through the astral aura.
- The azuric demons can enter mainly through the spiritual aura.

Weaknesses in any of these three auras create holes/passageways for demons. Such passageways are also created by the use of many drugs (see Addendum). Such weaknesses or passageways are also the cause of hyper-

---

[*] In Germany, Neural Therapy is considered part of conventional medicine. In spite of this, there are very few people in Norway who are familiar with this form of therapy. In British publications, it is referred to as Instantaneous Phenomenon Therapy. The reason for this name is that the results of a successful treatment often manifest within seconds.

Dr Ferdinand Hünecke, the medical doctor who discovered and publicized the method in 1928, researched it until his death in 1968.

sensibility. Hyper-sensibility is a 'disease' through which we are too easily influenced by the external spirits or forces of the world or by radiation of all kinds. Spirits, demons, radiation of electromagnetic or spiritual origin, the deep layers of the Earth, sounds or other sensory influences may enter or influence us through auric weaknesses. Then our skin will react as if sunburnt, as if radiated. The rays of the sun, the radiation from plutonium and so on are also, in fact, spirits or demons.

- Ahrimanic demons come from radiation of electric origins.
- Luciferic demons come from radiation of magnetic origin.
- Luciferic and ahrimanic demons both come from radiation as electro-magnetic radiation.
- Azuric demons come from radiation from nuclear sources.

Through the weaknesses or passageways in one or more of our auras, different demons may enter. Then they create disease for the person in question and for all entities connected to that person. The family, the animals, even trees and plants, may suffer in the presence of such demons.

Example

I was asked to help an elderly lady living together with her husband far away in the woods. As she was hypersensitive to all kinds of electrical radiation (ahrimanic influences), they had been living in this cabin in the woods for 20 years, without any kind of electricity. They lived a good life there, but she wanted to be less sensitive.

I observed her carefully. Her etheric aura, which in sound and healthy people is closed and envelops the whole body, had a huge opening on the top of her head. For this reason, she had strong hyper-sensibility to electricity, as the ahrimanic demons that come from electrical sources enter especially through the etheric aura.

As we sat there talking, a plane flew over the cabin about 6,000 metres above us. Immediately, she became red in her face, her breathing became difficult and her eyes started to water. She showed a typical allergic reaction.

To be certain that it was not a psychosomatic reaction, I decided to test her. I gathered a small 'package' of etheric energy (this was done mentally of course), lifted the package directly over her head and dropped it through the huge opening over her head. Immediately she almost fainted and became hyper-allergic. She was definitely not pretending.

The treatment for this condition is to close the hole in the etheric aura.

I told her this and gave her instructions as to how to close the big auric hole hovering over her head.

These instructions were:

1. *Always to wear a hat.*
2. *To wear a little cap of pure wool under the hat (a little like the skullcap that some Jews wear).*
3. *To keep her hair short (as the hair may act as antennae to the spiritual world).*
4. *To have a strong conscious focus on diminishing the size of the hole.*
5. *To hold her hand over her head during allergic reactions.*

I must add that she did not want to follow any of my advice, and today she is still living there, in her little un-electrified cabin deep in the woods, north of my home.

Chapter Three

How to Stop or Prevent the Demonic Effects of Earth Radiation

As we know from Chapter Two, earth radiation itself, or rather the demons characterized by or fed from earth radiation, is a mysterious force that causes sickness, especially if we are exposed to the influence of this force in an intensive or long-lasting way.

As we saw from the quotations in the last chapter, Rudolf Steiner introduced the concept of 'geographic medicine' in lectures he held in St Gallen in 1917. Here he described forces coming from the deep layers of the earth which nourish and strengthen the ahrimanic forces, entities or demons that abide within us.

In olden times, people knew that there were innumerable earthbound entities in the form of elementals, living within and of the earth itself. These entities were usually considered harmful to humans and animals. As the time of the Enlightenment dawned upon us in its full strength (from 1500 AD), we stopped believing in elemental beings and the mysterious forces that reside in the deep layers of the Earth. The pathological radiation coming from the Earth was explained as being electro-magnetic. Such radiation, such as we find under high voltage lines and the emanations from cell phones, is pathological to all life forms. However, the problem was that advanced machines and devices made for the detection of electro-magnetic radiation were able only to detect a minor part of all the radiation that sensitive people, dowsers and clairvoyants were able to map out. This led to the conclusion that dowsers discovered radiation that in actual fact did not exist—that they were shams and cheats. This of course is not right.

Again, in our modern times we must accept that the physical world is a manifestation of the spiritual world. All radiation is related to spiritual beings, to elementals and to demons. As people have strived against and tried to shield themselves from this demonic radiation for many years, we will start by taking a look at the experiences gathered by this group of sensitive people. This chapter will thus deal with and explore the following:

1. Old concepts and understanding of earth radiation and its prevention and shielding (before 1500).
2. Old concepts and understanding of earth radiation and its prevention and shielding (1500–1850).

3. Modernistic and 'scientific' concepts relating to shielding methods from earth radiation (1900–2000).
4. Spiritual concepts and shielding methods concerning earth radiation (2000+).

There is a vast amount of information that has come from olden times on how to protect oneself from the influence of different kinds of demons.

The descriptions of earth radiation from before 1500 AD were highly spiritual. People were totally aware of the existence of such entities and there were numerous ways to protect oneself and others against them.

These methods were mainly of spiritual origin, using special and magical words (as described in the *Kalevala*), special poems, ritual offerings (as described in the *Edda*) or magical rites. People burnt special herbs and made and wore special masks to scare away demons.

From the Reformation up to the middle of the nineteenth century (1500–1850), conventional scientists attributed these forces from the earth in terms of physical electromagnetic phenomena. They acknowledged physical radiation but did not acknowledge spiritual radiation, as their instruments could not detect or measure it. Modern atheistic science makes the same mistake. Its instruments cannot detect or measure spiritual energies, and therefore, God, soul and the spirit world do not exist!

In recent years, especially during the twentieth century, most dowsers also believe that the earth radiation lines they detect are of electromagnetic nature. The devices that they have developed to detect and shield those forces are based on this assumption.

However, since the year 2000 we are discovering increasingly that all geopathic radiation and noxious 'physical electromagnetic' phenomena (for example brain cancer associated with cell phones) involve noxious spiritual forces. We then see that all earth radiation, both the more physical and the spiritual, have spiritual causes. The physical electromagnetic radiation always has an ahrimanic and demonic cause, whereas the spiritual radiation can have both a spiritual and a demonic origin.

The literature from national dowser groups in America, Europe and Australia is full of case histories of disorders, mainly human, that were caused by various forms of earth radiation. These were detected by electronic devices and/or by spiritual means. Because of this diversity, the devices used to eliminate or neutralize the radiation have been very varied. They range from 'earthing the radiation' (using copper wire), to 'spiking the radiation lines' (hammering iron rods into the ground, upstream of the aquifers that run under the geopathic zone), to spiritual or shamanic methods (using prayer/incantations/symbols etc. to release the demon/noxious entity).

Of the human or animal disorders or symptoms caused by earth radiation, 90 per cent responded positively within weeks after correction or elimination of the earth radiation. The general opinion among dowsers is that, when more usual methods of conventional and holistic medicine fail to help a patient, one should always check his/her sleeping and work places for noxious radiation from geopathic zones.

In recent years, some people have shielded their homes against all types of radiation. This is not a good practice as it also removes the earth's normal radiation that is necessary and health-giving (later we will see that we need it for our 'karma'). Total shielding from normal radiation can have problematic consequences for our biorhythms.

Dowsers emphasize that we should try to avoid Earth radiation only in areas where they are excessive or noxious. There are four main ways to do this:

a) Vary the influence
b) Move away from the influence
c) Shield from the influence
d) 'Dissolve' the influence (spiritually, especially e.g. in haunted houses).

- *Vary the influence:* This is probably the best way to treat the disorder. In practice, we see that disorders occur when the body is subjected to the same type of frequency or radiation over a long period of time. We can avoid chronic exposure to the negative influence if we regularly vary the place in which animals are confined, our work place or the location of the bed. Sleeping with the head direction turned north for one month and then south for the next month can also do this. If one has a double bed, one can additionally change the side one sleeps on.
- *Move away from the influence:* If we want to move away from the noxious zone, we first must confirm its exact location. Then we must find a place where the radiation is absent, or milder.
- *Shielding from the influence:* Because of limited space or money, most people have difficulty finding new places to sleep or rest, or to vary those places regularly. In such cases, shielding can be useful, although seldom with lasting effect.
- Dissolving *the influence* is also possible if one understands the origin of the radiation, as in the case of haunted houses or other such places. The origin of most of the radiation comes from ill deeds performed in the past. If we can ask for forgiveness for those ill deeds, the radiation may totally dissolve.

Shielding is based on three methods:

- Diversion of the radiation
- Accumulation and discharge of the radiation
- Modification of the radiation.

1. *Diversion of the radiation:* To divert geopathic radiation we can use an electric cable, usually a copper wire. The wire is tightened around the horsebox, the stable, the bed, the chair or the place to be shielded, and is earthed by being soldered to a metal water pipe, or to a copper spike buried in the earth. Other materials that seem to shield or divert radiation include turf (peat), swamp turf (AR) and lead plates. (The Älma Company in Sweden market bed pads of swamp turf that seem to stop or modify the effects of earth radiation.) Also, lead plates that are thick enough may block earth radiation. German experiments suggested that the plates must be several cms thick. Thin lead plates (a few mms thick) may be effective initially but they lose their blocking effect after a few months (which, actually, applies to all methods). This may be due to micro-perforations, which can be seen by electron microscopy.

2. *Accumulation and discharge of the radiation:* A type of accumulator made from plastic layers seems to be effective; 15–20 layers of plastic are placed under the bed. This seems to function for a few months (as all other methods do). I do not know how this could be achieved for large animals, but it should be easy to do for small animals and humans. After some months, one must 'discharge' the plastic by putting it on damp ground, or by washing it.

3. *Modification of the radiation:* Magnets may be used to neutralize or modify noxious radiation, especially if the radiation is of ahrimanic origin. The magnets will then strengthen the luciferic radiation, and thus weaken the ahrimanic. If we expose the radiation to a magnetic field, it seems that we can modify it so that it does not cause illness. I have seen several different arrangements of strong and weak magnets that seem to have modified geopathic ahrimanic radiation, so that the pathological effect was dispersed. The use of turf falls into this category, since it appears that turf modifies radiation, rather than shielding or diverting it. Why this should be so is difficult to understand. The only explanation I can think of is that the turf is plant material that is 5–10,000 years old, and in those times the luciferic influence was stronger that the ahrimanic. As such, the turf works like a magnet.

NB: it is possible that all the different ways of shielding places from earth radiation work because of the intention of the person who installs the devices. This will explain that almost all types of devices work, and that the effects vanish after some time.

The only truly effective way to dissolve radiation is to acknowledge the spiritual origin of the radiation and to ask or pray for forgiveness for the ill deeds done, so that the radiation is permanently dissolved.

Example
There was one very strong radiation zone that affected several people along the coast of Norway. A group of dowsers found out that this radiation was created in the 1500s by a group of Spanish seamen capturing some women in the north-east coast of Norway and taking them as slaves to Spain. When this connection was realized and forgiveness was asked for, the whole line of radiation dissolved and disappeared.

The above will be elaborated later, when the spiritual origin of earth radiation is discussed.

Tracing noxious radiation

Four important methods are used to trace noxious radiation:

- Divining instruments
- Technical instruments to detect electromagnetic distortions
- Bioassay: the use of living organisms such as mice, fish, insects or plants to observe their growth and wellbeing under the influence of noxious radiation (such organisms can of course 'detect' all kinds of radiation, from radioactive to spiritual)
- Sensitivity and/or clairvoyance, which is necessary for tracing all spiritual radiation or influences.

Divining instruments
As recorded over aeons of time, one can find noxious zones by dowsing or divining. The dowser holds a divining rod (Y-stick), or other divining instruments such as a pendulum, rubbing pad or angle irons in the hands. When the body's autonomic system senses a noxious influence, it increases muscle spasm. This causes the divining instrument to move or behave differently, thus indicating the location of the noxious influence.

A personal comment and example
The explanation that the body's autonomic system senses a noxious influence and reacts, is the usually accepted one. However, I have personally seen cases where the divining instrument has been violently torn out of the hands of a person when they pass an area of earth radiation. Therefore, I believe there must be other, far stronger, forces at play. In one case, after being torn out of a woman's hands, the Y-stick flew

with great speed through the room, finally smashing into the wall with great force. After this, the dowser fainted. This happened after I had 'strengthened' the effect of the dowsing by using a picture of the moon that I had placed on the body of the dowsing woman. This showed me that the usual scientific explanation is not sufficient in explaining the effects of dowsing. There are far stronger and unknown spiritual forces working within earth radiation.

Technical equipment to detect electromagnetic distortions

If a transistor radio is tuned to 'white noise' with its antenna extended, the noise may change when the searcher moves over a zone that is distorted by earth radiation. Other electronic measuring equipment, such as a sensitive magnetometer that can register the more physical types of ahrimanic earth radiation, gives a more objective and quantitative proof than divining rods. However, this equipment is expensive and hard to locate. Research within a large range of electronic devices shows that they have the added disadvantage that they do not differentiate qualitatively between the earth radiation that causes disease and the earth radiation that is harmless. Also, they are unable to detect the most important earth radiation, namely the spiritual earth radiation from the deep layers of the earth. Skilled dowsers who acknowledge the spiritual side of earth radiation, however, do have this ability as an innate reaction, concerning both electromagnetic and spiritual radiation.

Tracing noxious influences by Bioassay using living organisms

German experiments on several hundred students between the two World Wars showed how some people reacted immediately upon being exposed to earth radiation. In these 'noxious zones', some people felt unwell or dizzy and saw dots in front of their eyes (vibrating sight). Blood pressure, measured before and during walking across areas of strong radiation, fell.

The dowsing reaction is transmitted via the parasympathetic part of the autonomic nervous system. This autonomic system, which usually is beyond voluntary control, controls respiration, heart rate, blood pressure, blood circulation, digestion and peristalsis of the digestive organs, urinary filtration rate and other organ functions. Measuring the blood pressure and heart rate can show the changes that occur when a sensitive person is exposed to a noxious area (see Rupert Sheldrake). We can prove the adverse effects of noxious radiation in a bioassay[*] with living organisms. Noxious influences stunt or alter adversely the immunity, growth or health of plants, humans and animals.

---

[*] The measurement of the concentration or potency of a substance by its effect on living cells or tissues.

The noxious influence is confirmed by noting its effects on the growth of hedges, plants or fruit trees, and where the plants thrive or fail and wither (see Peter Tompkins and Christopher Bird, *The Secret Life of Plants*). This method takes a long time and is not as convenient to prevent illness as the other methods described above.

Finding pathological radiation through sensitivity and/or clairvoyance

This method leads directly over into the last and third part of these descriptions, namely the spiritual explanation and understanding of Earth radiation.

For me, this method is one of the most interesting as it points to the real origins of radiation, namely not physical but spiritual. It can be performed in several ways, but all ways require that we have entered the spiritual world through dividing our thinking, feeling and will.

We do this:

- Through pulsing (see pulse diagnosis page 32f).
- Through 'seeing'.
- Through a number of other means such as:

  —Smelling (like a metal smell).
  —Hearing (like glass cracking).

What is it that we cannot detect physically, but only detect with spiritual means? It is the spiritual foundation of earth radiation.

Earth radiation is the pathological expression or manifestation of ahrimanic beings, in the form of elementals, demons or higher ahrimanic demons, including the being of Ahriman himself.

These influences come from:

1. The depths of the Earth, where they were created or placed eons ago.
2. From deeds performed before the human race manifested or was born in the flesh (for example the deeds of the Brownies*).
3. From deeds performed by human beings such as anger, greed, jealousy, lying, murder, fighting, and so on.

Finding the spiritual radiation from past sins or from the ahrimanic beings in the deeper layers of the Earth is only possible through clairvoyance and

---

* The Brownies are elemental beings found in a number of places in nature. They have no connections to humans but stay within themselves. They are *very* old, and are possibly created by the deeds of former human races like the Neanderthals. They form communities with their own infrastructure, have no clothes, are small and hairy, and speak little. I have seen two colonies of these creatures.

spiritual sensitivity. As most of the radiation has its origin in the past deeds of humans, the shielding or dispersing of this kind of radiation must be based according to spiritual means.

Only by loving and forgiving the past ill deeds committed, preferably in the name of the Christ, can such radiation permanently be dissolved (much the same as dissolving the ahrimanic and the luciferic demons through the Middle Point—the Christ Point treated with Christ Consciousness.

We need to stop thinking of Earth radiation as 'radiation' understood by scientists of modern times, and in addition name it in a completely different way. Modern scientists have repeatedly commented that if it really is radiation, it should be detectable through modern radiation detectors. Of course, some 'radiation' of cosmic and earthly origin is detectable, and that is of electromagnetic origin. But this kind of radiation is not what we are mainly dealing with here.

A Buddhist way of seeing the radiation and how to relate to it

The reason for describing the Buddhistic viewpoint is that their description matches my own observations quite well. The main source for this description is found in the writings of Sri Ananda Acharia, a Buddhist monk that came to Norway from India in 1910, and lived his whole life in Alvdal, Norway, where he tried to build a university based on peace, love and Buddhism. In his book, *How Karlima Rani Spoke*, Chapter 9, he describes the geopathic radiation as follows:

> There are strong forces coming from the cosmos to the earth. These 'radiation-energies' change every two hours. They may be used in a positive way by living organisms and humans when they are absorbed directly. The radiation from the cosmos is of three types called *Seor*, *Boom* and *Beor*.
>
> If this radiation is not taken into the physical body and used directly, it enters the earth and is then reflected by the demonic inhabitants of the deeper layers of the earth. It then becomes materialized and changed by the karmic deeds of human beings, and consequently becomes malevolent.
>
> This is the origin of earth radiation. It then creates disease.

'Old' medieval spiritual ways of protection

Many spiritual methods of protecting oneself from demonic influences are described in literature deriving from medieval times.

- Imagine yourself to be a fully armoured knight, holding a huge long sword. Stand towards the north and touch the ground with the tip of the sword. Where the tip touches the ground a flame lights up. Then slowly turn west and continue through south, east and back to north again, thus creating a full circle around you with the tip of the sword. When the circle is complete, you will find yourself standing in the middle of a flaming circle. This will protect you for about twelve hours, after which the whole procedure has to be repeated.
- Imagine a mirror surrounding you, reflecting back all radiation coming in. This procedure will protect you for 24 hours.[*]

Example
I was working as a veterinarian in Bodø, Northern Norway. As described in the Introduction, I was in a barn treating a cow with milk fever (hypocalcemia), when the cow suddenly died. Fourteen days later, I was again in the same barn, and the same thing happened. Fourteen days later still, this repeated itself for the third time. After realizing that the cause of these three deaths was black magic cast by the neighbour, I then performed a ritual isolating the whole barn from evil. I did this by going around the entire barn imagining that I was a knight in shining armour, encircling the whole area with my sword. Where the sword touched the ground, flames shot up, and after completing the circle, the barn and the cows were protected by a wall of fire. After that no more cows died.

Is it possible to treat the elementals and demons within earth radiation through the Middle Point, through Christ Consciousness?

Earth radiation appears to the spiritual eye, or at least to mine, as black snakes curling and moving along the surface of the Earth. They must not be mistaken or wrongly seen as the energetic bonds between trees and plants, which are described in my book *Poplar.*[†] The bonds between trees are much lighter and not so dark, but still look very similar to 'earth radiation snakes', as both are moving through the floor of the forest. The 'tree-snakes' are relatively easy to enter with the consciousness, and it is possible to then travel within the energy. Travelling in the left direction takes you back in time. Travelling to the right is something I have rarely dared to do, as I fear it might take me forward to future times, and I consider the future belonging to

---

[*] Many more methods are described in the book, *Clavicula Salomonis.*
[†] CreateSpace, 2015.

higher powers than mine.* Within these energetic streams of the trees, we may experience the secret of 'the double stream of time stream'.†

I will try to describe the black snakes that are the expression of earth radiation. They are seen as darker black, not transparent like the tree energy snakes. To enter inside the earth radiation snakes is not advisable as they are of a malignant, ahrimanic nature. They are the 'web' described in the *Edda*, the web that the *Norns* are weaving. They are the past deeds of all humans, the karma of each and every one of us. This karma of past deeds can be healed by asking forgiveness in the name of the Christ.

Is it possible to treat the elementals and demons in plants and trees through the Middle Point or through Christ Consciousness?

For many years I have 'pulsed' trees. Ferdinand Niessen (a German colleague) once made me aware that all trees had a weakness in the Water element, about a third from the top. I pondered for years on why all trees had this lack of the Water element in this particular place. Then I realized that all humans and animals do have a deficiency of Water where the luciferic demon or elemental abides, as Lucifer *is* Fire and Light, which is

---

* See the lecture by Rudolf Steiner on *The Apocalypse of St John*, 17 June, 1908: 'And if man gives himself up to this force he grows into the spiritual world from which he has descended. He will ascend again to where the initiate's vision can already reach today. Man will divest himself of what belongs to the senses when he penetrates into the spiritual world. The candidate who was initiated in ancient times could see in retrospect the far past of spirit-life; those who are initiated in the Christian sense through receiving the impulse of Christ Jesus are enabled to see what becomes of this earthly world of ours when humanity acts in the sense of the Christ Impulse. As one can look back to earlier conditions, so, starting from the coming of Christ, one can look into the farthest future. Consciousness will alter again, there will be a new relation of the spiritual to the sense world. Earlier initiation was directed to time past, to age-old wisdom; Christian initiation reveals the future to one who is to be initiated. That is a necessity; man is to be initiated not only in wisdom or in feelings but in his will. For then he knows what he is to do, he can set himself a goal for the future. Ordinary everyday people set themselves aims for the afternoon, for the evening or the morning; the spiritual man is able, out of spiritual principles, to set himself distant aims which pulse through his will and make his forces quicken. To set goals before humanity means in the true, highest sense, in the sense of the original Christ principle, to grasp Christianity esoterically. In this way it was grasped by the one who has written the great principle of the initiation of the will—the writer of the Apocalypse. We misunderstand the Apocalypse if we do not understand it as the impulse given for the future, for action and deed.'
† The double stream of time is one of the most important secrets we should know about when entering the spiritual world. Time can go either way, both from the future towards the past, and from the past towards the future.

opposed to Water. In connection with Lucifer, we always find a deficient kidney-energy. The luciferic demon is almost always to be found around a third down from the head.

We can find the ahrimanic elemental one third from the root of the tree, and also from the tail of animals and humans; or, if the individual is diseased, we find the demon. Here we also find a deficiency in the etheric forces of the tree (as the ahrimanic elemental demands its place) and in the wood element, in the liver-energy of the tree.

When we thus pulse a tree, it is important that we do not pulse the tree a third from the root or a third from the top, otherwise we always get either a deficiency in the liver or in the kidney. This is the same in animals and humans. We have to enter the heart to get a correct pulse finding.

To treat the tree from the Middle Point, we have to 'needle' it (this can be done mentally, of course) on the Middle Point between the kidney-deficiency and the liver-deficiency. Then both the deficiencies often disappear.

The phenomena of smoke and smell and their relation to demons

The use of smoke in religious connections is as old as humanity itself.
In the Old Testament it is told that both Cain and Abel made burnt sacrifices to God, and the way that the smoke behaved was an indication as to whether God accepted their offerings or not. Abel's smoke rose upwards into the air, whilst the smoke from Cain's offering stayed close to the earth. My understanding of this is that Abel's smoke was able to drive away the earth-bound spirits and open his mind to God. Cain, on the other hand, was destined to work with the earth, to struggle his way through the earthly domain and as such also fight both the luciferic and the ahrimanic demons.

A combination of smoke and smell is essential for the effect of the procedure, even though the smoke seems to be the most important part of the two. I have always felt the peace and quiet that descends after making a campfire. Once the campfire is lit and the smoke wafts and is smelled amongst the trees, it feels as if the camp has become a home. One feels settled and at peace as the fire burns. The evil spirits are driven away and the good spirits are called upon. One's soul falls into a state of peacefulness.

In many different religious ceremonies dedicated to the gods, incense is often used around the altar to keep the demons away and possibly transform them. The American Indians often burn white sage to cleanse the body before ritual ceremonies.

Example 1

I had a left eye retinal loosening, which resulted in being driven to Oslo in an ambulance and having an eye operation. The days after the operation were painful, and I felt miserable. Both the ahrimanic and the luciferic 'disease demons' were closing in on my left eye, and the luciferic demons were causing me pain. I made a fire in the fireplace of my living room, and suddenly felt a strong urge to close the chimney and let the room be filled with smoke. I felt better and better, despite the protests from my wife. The rest of the day I felt very well, although one could smell the smoke in the house, which was not a particularly pleasant aroma. The next day, however, I felt miserable again. Pondering on my situation, I suddenly had an enlightening inspiration: the smoke! I went to fetch a piece of Palo Santo wood used for burning incense and set fire to it. When I blew out the flame, the room was filled with the smoke of the incense. I waved the smoking piece of wood in front, beside and behind me, and immediately both the luciferic and the ahrimanic demons of the disease loosened their grip. For me, this was a huge revelation.

Example 2

A German doctor I once knew specialized in 'smelling' diseases. He cured or treated the ailments by adding different etheric oils or fragrances to the bedclothes of the patient, which then counteracted the smell of the disease. The smell drove the demons of the disease away, in the same way that the plant spirits do if they resemble the disease-demon. It's all about driving the disease demons away, although in doing it this way, we do not know where they are translocated.

Example 3

I was in Seattle during a veterinary acupuncture congress. Four Native Americans who also attended the congress had asked me up to their room on the fourteenth floor to participate in their ceremony of smoking the peace pipe. We were sitting in the room in a circle, passing the pipe around. I had several times assured myself that the tobacco used was not of hallucinogenic or mind-changing plants but rather consisted only of non-toxic herbs and tobacco. The smoke had its effect in the room. The atmosphere was markedly lighter. The Chief called for the good spirits of the Earth and asked the demonic spirits to go away. Then, in the middle of the ceremony, the door to the room was opened and a traditionally dressed Native American entered the room. I was amazed by his presence as he wore the full, feather-ornamented, traditional dress, in the middle of Seattle, on the fourteenth floor of one of the finest hotels. He closed the door and stood for a while, gazing at the circle. I asked the person beside me what he was doing there. He looked at me with astonishment asking, 'Do you see him? If so, you are the first white man ever to see him'. The smoke and the ritual had cleared the room of ahrimanic and evil spirits so that this old shaman could appear.

In all cultures and even in orthodox services, the burning of incense has been used to clear away evil spirits and demons. The North American Indians burnt sage to clean their bodies of 'bad energy' before entering sacred sites or ceremonies. This also brings some insight into why smoking is such a huge and worldwide habit. It simply keeps the demons at bay.

All my life I have wondered why people smoked. When asking smokers, they told me that they felt better when smoking, still unable to tell me specifically how and in what way better. They simply felt 'relieved'. Now this makes perfect sense. The smoking/smoke pushes the demons away, and then of course the smoker feels better (although the effect on the lungs will attract disease-demons).

Smelling the Middle Point (Clairalience)

I once gave an eight-day course in Florida on how to find and treat the Middle. Some days before, I had given a three-day course in New York, where one of the participants had insisted on smelling all the patients. She claimed she was able to smell the different diseases. I had observed her somewhat unusual diagnostic method but considered it a little bizarre. Then, when teaching in Florida, as the students were discussing how to find the anatomical Middle Point—most of them being unable to 'see' the Middle as I could—we were discussing the possibility of feeling the ahrimanic and the luciferic demons, of seeing them, of hearing them or of smelling them. I suddenly got the idea of trying to smell them. I breathed out, and with a long and constant inhalation through my nose I moved my face in a constant speed over the back of the dog we had as a patient at the table at the time. To my surprise, it was very easy to smell the Middle Point. From the cranial region to the Middle Point, the smell was very typical. At the exact Middle Point, the smell changed to a pleasant odour and immediately from the caudal to the Middle, the smell changed again to a somewhat more 'physical', doglike or even pathological smell. I asked the other participants to do this 'sniffing-test', and about 30% of the participants could clearly recognize the three different smells. Hence a new method was found to localize the Middle Point. I called this method the 'sniffing diagnostic test'.

Medical plants viewed from the aspect of demons and plant spirits

Demons versus plant spirits

If we observe or 'see' demons, they all have a personal or individual look. The demons of special diseases look very similar, as in the group of 'flu demons', 'common cold demons', and so on. However, they still do have a personal look, differing from person to person.

If we consider the plant spirits, they also have a definite look. The spirits of plants within the same family look alike but are not identical. Many of the flower spirits look quite pretty. As regards the medical plants, however, this is not so. Plant spirits of poisonous and medical plants look quite frightening.

The poisonous plant spirits, at least for those plants that are medicinal, look very much like the demons that create the diseases. Plant spirits that look identical to the 'disease bringing spirits', can cure the related diseases. We may say that 'like cures like', just as Hahnemann[*] postulated, as did the people in medieval times who believed that plants carried a 'signature' that indicated which diseases they worked against. This doctrine of signatures[†] has a real background for those who can see spirits and demons. Lay people have used this knowledge, but being unable to see the spirits and demons, they were stuck with the outer physical appearance of the plant and the disease. Consequently, this deep insight lost its meaning, and today the doctrine of signatures is presented as pure superstition.

People knew this in past times, that like cures (frightens) like, that similar spirits scare each other. That is why they made pictures or sculptures of small demons on the corners of churches, as they believed that these images would scare the real demons away. In the plant world, this works in much the same way. We have to give the patient a medical plant that carries the spirit that looks similar to the demon that carries the disease.

The plant spirits are not easily frightened by the disease spirits. Indeed, they are quite brave.

The disease demons are much less brave, at least in most cases. As such, the plant spirit wins over the disease demon.

The phenomena of shivering and jolting and their relation to the release of demons (or, as in homeopathy, the translocation of healing spirits)

In 1982 I participated in a Qigong course, planned to last for three days. There were about 70 participants. An Asian instructor, a specialist in his field and a clairvoyant, led the course. For the first exercise, he asked us to

[*] Christian Friedrich Samuel Hahnemann (1755–1843) was a German physician, best known for creating the system of alternative medicine called homeopathy.
[†] The doctrine of signatures is a medieval law in herbal medicine that the physiognomy and the appearance of a plant will indicate against which disease it will act curatively.

stand in a special and exact Qigong stance. This was the opening stance to free oneself of any attached spirits (demons).

As directed, all participants stood in this somewhat unpleasant stance. After a few minutes, the other participants began to tremble and shiver and groan as the stance and the trembling became more and more unpleasant. Everyone else began to tremble and shake, as if they were having an epileptic fit, and the groaning intensified. I was somewhat amazed and embarrassed because I was not trembling, nor did I have an unpleasant feeling. I looked around and felt totally alienated. Something must be wrong with me. I asked the instructor what I was doing wrong.

He told me that I did nothing wrong. This Qigong stance was designed to expel the demons attached to the body and this struggle caused the trembling and jolting. Upon the initiation of a fight against demons, the demons and the body of the host always shiver and jolt. 'You,' he said, 'seem not to have any attached demons. You can go home.' And so, I did.

I noted later that a host's body always shakes, some less and some more vigorously, when my acupuncture treatment causes demons to be expelled. Indeed, this strange phenomenon of shivering can also arise when demons translocate (change their place of residence) within the body. In so-called demon exorcism, as carried out by the Catholic Church, there are many eyewitness descriptions recounting how the body of the person from whom the demon is expelled always shivers and jolts.

This phenomenon is also seen in homeopathy. For many years I wondered why, when making the remedy, it had to be shaken so vigorously between each of the potency stages. After I had begun to 'see' the elemental forces in medical plants as well as in diseases, I entered into a deeper understanding of the procedure of making a homeopathic remedy.

The characteristic or look of the elemental beings within the medical plant used for making the remedy, looks very much like the pathological being that causes the disease. This is the basis of the homeopathic law of *similia similibus curentur.*[*] Homeopaths know or postulate that the 'energy' of the plant or the metal mysteriously translocate into the water when the dilution is shaken. This shaking enables the spirit of the healing plant to enter or translocate into the remedy. This is then called 'potentization' i.e. it makes the water 'potent'.

---

[*] The fundamental principle of homeopathy is found in the sentence *similia similibus curentur* or 'like cures like'. More precisely, a homeopathic remedy cures a disease whose symptoms resemble the symptoms evoked in a healthy body by a toxic dose of the agent itself.

Mediumship and demons

As I have stated several times, the demons and the adversaries are
'allowed' by cosmic law to work on human beings and to influence them.
Demons do not have to respect the free will of humans. The benevolent
entities and forces, however, are obliged to respect the free will and free
choice of all humans under the same cosmic law.

Rudolf Steiner is quite clear about the use of mediums. In his lectures
on *True and False Paths in Spiritual Investigation*,[*] Lecture eight, 'Potential
Aberrations in Spiritual Investigation', given on 9 August 1924, he stated
that mediums are openings and gateways for ahrimanic and luciferic
forces to enter into the world of humans. He said:

> We can only know what the elementary beings are, the progeny of the
> ahrimanic powers, when we enter into the world immediately bor-
> dering our own. These beings manifest through mediums. They take
> possession of the mediums and in this way temporarily enter our world.
> If we contact them through a human medium only, we learn to know
> them in a world that should really be foreign to them; we do not know
> them in their true form. Spiritual revelations are undoubtedly trans-
> mitted, but it is impossible to understand them when they issue from a
> world to which they do not belong. The deceptive and highly hal-
> lucinative element in everything connected with mediumistic con-
> sciousness is explained by the fact that those who contact these beings
> have no understanding of their real nature. Now, because they enter
> the world in this way, a unique destiny is reserved to these beings. The
> knowledge of the universe that I have described serves to enlarge our
> field of knowledge. When we enter the world of the dead, we traverse
> demonic forests of poisonous plants like *Colchicum autumnale* (meadow
> saffron), *Digitalis purpurea* (purple foxglove), *Datura stramonium* (thorn
> apple), and so on. The poisonous plants are moribund plants, species
> that are dying out, with no possibility of future development. In future
> times they will be replaced by other poisonous species. The poisonous
> species of today are already dying out in our epoch. The epoch of
> course is of long duration, but these poisonous plants have the seeds of
> death within them. And this will be the fate of all vegetation. When we
> survey the world of vegetation with spiritual vision, we perceive forces
> of growth and development with a dynamic urge towards the future
> and a world that is dying and doomed to perish. And so, it is with the
> beings that take possession of mediums. They detach themselves from

_____

[*] Rudolf Steiner Press, London, 1985.

their companions, whose task is to carry over the present into a distant future. Through the agency of mediums, they invade the world of the present, and are there caught up in the destiny of the earth and sacrifice their future mission. In this way, they deprive man to a large extent of his future mission. And this is what faces us when we understand the real nature of mediumism, for mediumism implies that the future shall perish in order that the present may be very important. When, therefore, we attend a séance with insight into the real occult relationships and into the true nature of the cosmos, we are at first astonished to find that the entire circle participating in a spiritistic manifestation is seemingly surrounded by poisonous plants. Every spiritualistic séance is surrounded in fact by a garden of poisonous plants, which no longer bear the same aspect as in the kingdom of the dead, but which grow up around the spiritualist circle, and from their fruits and flowers demonic beings are seen to emerge. Such is the experience of the clairvoyant at a spiritualistic séance. For the most part, he goes through a kind of cosmic thicket of poisonous plants that are activated from within and are part animal. Only by their forms do we recognize that they are poisonous plants. We learn from this how everything at work within this mediumistic form that ought to advance the course of human evolution and bear fruit in the future, is relegated to the present where it does not belong. In the present, it works to the detriment of humanity. Such is the inner mystery of mediumism, a mystery of which we shall learn more in the course of these lectures.

It has become more and more apparent that the ahrimanic demons are very intelligent and they change and translocate to avoid being seen or attacked.

The classic séances as described by Rudolf Steiner in these lectures are not performed today as they were a hundred years ago. Today, the demons have taken on the disguise of modern times and mediums that are hysterical or half-unconscious are rare. Today, the mediums seem to be totally conscious and intelligent people that channel information from the spiritual worlds.

How can we best protect ourselves today?

There are several ways to protect ourselves through connecting to the forces of good; by having a greater knowledge, insight into and consciousness of the good forces, unlike the old methods of rituals and fighting evil:

- Pray to your guiding spirits, your angels.
- Do not fight the Adversaries. Rather, have total trust in the forces of good.
- Try to help and transform the demon (love thy enemy).
- Develop knowledge of the inhabitants and existence of the spiritual worlds, especially about the adversaries.
- Seek insight into the workings and laws of the spiritual worlds. These are very different from the laws of the physical world.
- Deepen consciousness of the presence of the spiritual worlds, especially the angelic world, but also of demons.
- Develop a strong 'I'-function (especially in the tenth, eleventh and twelfth layers of the heart, the Christ level). At this level the demons have no power at all.

A simple method to detect or diagnose if the patient has been or is under the influence of demonic earth radiation

I have developed, or rather found, a simple method that may detect a positional influence of earth radiation. Patients that do not react to treatment might be under such influence, unless we treat from the twelfth layer of the heart. Here the demonic earth radiation, old scars, physical or mental traumas have no power in stopping or interfering with any kind of treatment.

With this method we also find out, in the case of there really being such an influence, at what angle the line of earth radiation hits the body. With this knowledge, we also know in what direction to move the person's bed (or the animal's) to avoid the pathological influence, and we will know which organ system is most vulnerable to this specific radiation.

To obtain all this information, we need a 5 × 5 cm plastic square. On this transparent sheet we should draw, in black waterproof ink, the figure illustrated below (the thin arrow is not to be drawn, it will be explained later).

This sheet is then held in front of the ear of the patient, while we

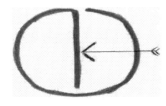

carefully control the pulse using the Nogiér method (RAC/VAS).* We then slowly turn the plastic sheet around 360°. At certain angles, there will be a distinct RAC/VAS. This reaction indicates that the patient is under the influence of pathological earth radiation.

The angle at which this radiation hits the body can be calculated in the following way:

- The ear resembles the body itself, with the lobe as the head and the top of the ear as the legs.
- This ear also carries the memory of the radiation, so that the pathological effect of the radiation is imprinted in the ear.
- The RAC/VAS occurs when the straight line in the drawing creates an angle of 90° with the imprinted radiation.
- If the RAC/VAS occurs as indicated in the diagram above, it means that the radiation crosses or hits the body 90° to the longitudinal axis (to the median plane).
- If the patient then sleeps with the head to the north and the feet to the south, then the radiation line will go east-west or west-east.
- Then we can know that the organ-system in danger is either the lungs or the liver (see table below).
- The patient will have to move his or her bed further towards the head or the feet. If they move the bed to the side, they will not avoid the radiation.

How to use this knowledge to treat patients

If we are to use this knowledge, we have to keep in mind that the direction of the radiation will decide which organ-system it will negatively affect. (The letters in the chart below refer to acupuncture points.)

So, then we will know which organ-system to stimulate, if the patient has been too long under the influence of demonic pathological earth radiation. We may treat the organ in question with herbs or acupuncture. The patient should also be removed from the radiation (although the radiation appears to follow the sick person).

---

* The pulse reaction, called the RAC or VAS by Dr Paul Nogiér, is an essential part of a thorough examination using auriculomedicine. This pulse response is a reflex from the skin to the heart or arterial blood circulation. Stimulation of the skin over a reactive area, a point or a weak structure, activates an autonomic reaction or recognition that induces a special VAS Pulse reaction. The VAS-reaction may be found anywhere at an artery. Dr Paul Nogiér, the 'father of Auriculotherapy', was a medical research scientist. As a physician he practiced acupuncture, psychotherapy, homeopathy and manipulative medicine. In 1951 his expertise in these techniques led to his discovery of Auricular therapy. Ten years later he developed Auricular medicine.

From north (radiation, electromagnetic or spiritual) will stimulate or hurt (a little will stimulate, too much will hurt)	KI BL
From south	HT, PC, SI, TH
From West	LU LI
From east	LV GB

Example

Dr Georg Bentze, my teacher in acupuncture, was a well-known doctor of alternative methods. He was once hired by the prison authorities of Oslo to help some of the prisoners feel more comfortable and to sleep better. He immediately started to map out all the lines of earth radiation under the beds of the prisoners. He noticed that there were more lines than usual, and that the strength of the lines was stronger than usual. He initiated and supervised moving all the beds of the prisoners. From the following night, they slept better, felt more relaxed and enjoyed life more. The prison administration was satisfied. When he returned one month later to assess the situation, he found, to his great surprise, that all the radiation lines had changed. They had followed the beds to their new positions, and now the situation was once again as it had been before. Dr Bentze was unsure as to how to deal with or explain this phenomenon. The whole experiment was forgotten by the prison authorities, as is usual with those who do not understand this kind of phenomena.

Today I understand this perfectly well, as the lines really are demonic beings, created by the life and behaviour of the prisoners themselves, and they belong to the karmic grid that each person carries around with him or her. That is why I no longer believe in isolating or shielding houses or bed-places from radiation. The only way to be free of the demonic radiation is to acknowledge the origin, to ask for forgiveness and change one's life. The radiation is a part of ourselves and must be loved and respected.

The knowledge about the directions was known in ancient times by all those who worked with animals and agriculture. Today, this knowledge is largely forgotten, or disparaged as pseudoscience. That is a great mistake.

A little radiation will stimulate, and there is always some radiation everywhere (there is always a presence of elemental beings, which we need). Standing or sleeping with the head towards a special direction will be beneficial to the organ-system in question, unless a demonic earth radiation also happens to come from that direction. Therefore, if a cow is standing with its head (the head being the receiver of cosmic radiation) towards north, the cow will receive energy that stimulates the kidneys. If the horse is standing with its head towards the east, the energy will stimulate the liver. Farmers in Austria knew this, and their old tradition was to let the cows stand with their heads towards the north, and horses towards east. Amazing!

This knowledge may also be used therapeutically. If a patient has problems with an organ system, it will be beneficial to stand or lie with the head in the stimulating direction of the organ system in question.

Chapter Four

How Do We Free or Defend Ourselves from Demons?

Demons and disease—A short description or characterization of ahrimanic and luciferic demons

The luciferic spirits have reached a higher state than man, and are therefore supersensible beings, whereas ahrimanic beings are in a lower state than man and, therefore, are 'subsensible' beings. The following information, derived from the research of Rudolf Steiner, will illustrate this point:

1. The ahrimanic impulse proceeds from a supersensible being different from the beings of Christ or Lucifer.
2. Lucifer is a being that has detached himself from the spiritual hosts of heaven after the separation of the Sun, whereas Ahriman had already broken away before the separation of the Sun and is an embodiment of quite different powers.
3. In certain occult teachings, the ahrimanic hordes are called the Azuras. These are the evil Azuras, who at a certain time fell away from the evolutionary path of the necessary Azuras (who endowed man with personality). It has already been indicated that these are spiritual beings that detached themselves from the evolution of the Earth before the separation of the Sun.
4. Lucifer brought man under the influence of the powers connected with Air and Water only, whereas it was Ahriman-Mephistopheles who has subjected man to the influence of far more deadly powers. The civilizations to come will see the appearance of many things connected with Ahriman's influence.
5. The influences of Ahriman therefore involve powers of a much lower nature than the influences of Lucifer. Lucifer's influences can never become as evil as the influences of Ahriman and of those beings that are connected with the powers of Fire.

When disease develops, it usually takes the path described below.

1) Improper living creates a weak and empty organ process, manifesting in a weakness of the etheric part of the process, which in acupuncture is called the Yin part.

First, one or more of our bodily processes are compromised. This happens through some wrong way of living. We might say by violating the Eightfold Path of Buddha: wrong thinking, wrong acting, wrong eating, wrong drinking, wrong feeling, wrong clothing and/or other wrongs we do in our lives. This creates a deficiency in some organic process, either of the heart, the pericardium, the kidneys, the lungs, the spleen or the liver.

2) An ahrimanic demon will enter or develop in this empty space.

In this void, emptiness or deficiency, foreign forces of a subhuman nature enter. These forces usually manifest in the shape of an ahrimanic demon. Sometimes, other demons might also manifest in a weakened organ, but that is not so usual.

3) When the ahrimanic dominion of the etheric part is achieved, the ahrimanic demon invites a luciferic demon to incarnate in the astral part of the process that it controls. The weakened organ process and the incarnated ahrimanic entity will not be able to perform the controlling action that a normal body process can. Because of this weakness, another organ process will come into excess, or we might say that the excess is created as the ahrimanic demon invites a luciferic demon in. This luciferic demon usually enters in the organ process controlled by the initial deficient process. This law was observed by the Chinese thousands of years ago and is expressed in their law of the five elements.

4) When the luciferic demon has invaded the astral or Yang part of the new process, it draws energy from the etheric Yin part, so that over time this also is weakened. If the ahrimanic and the luciferic demons incarnate in the same organ, it often results in especially destructive diseases like cancer. As cancer is the cooperation between the ahrimanic and luciferic demons, and this may vary from patient to patient, drugs that strengthen either the ahrimanic or the luciferic demons may help greatly in fighting this terrible disease. Today the ahrimanic demons are usually the strongest and most prolific in disease creating, so substances that strengthen the luciferic demons in a general way may be positive in cancer.

In this connection, it is interesting to observe that many therapists and scientists claim that cannabidiol or oil from cannabis can cure cancer. Cannabis is one of the substances that strengthen the luciferic demons most effectively. If it is smoked together with tobacco, it might have the opposite effect. Tobacco strengthens the ahrimanic demons, and by combining the two, the cancer-inducing marriage of Ahriman and Lucifer may get closer, and the cancer may get worse. Art also strengthens and invigorates the luciferic spirits, which in the case of disease may be called 'demons'. This is why art may also work in healing patients suffering from cancer, as developed in art therapy.

In pulse diagnosis, we have an expression: 'destructive energy'. This is a very special feeling of the pulse. This destructive energy is created when the luciferic demon captures or takes hold of the ahrimanic one.

Example

A dog had been diagnosed with rectal cancer and had been treated by the veterinarian without success. The local veterinarian wanted to euthanize the dog, but the owner wanted to give the dog one last chance. She arrived at my home in the afternoon. The cancer was ugly looking. The anus was swollen to the size of a large grapefruit, partly ulcerated. The dog had problems walking. I knew ordinary treatment would be useless. I turned my intention and gaze in to the demon world and saw an ugly-looking demon right in front of the cancer. As the owner had lived with Native Americans and believed in demons, I told her what I had seen. She said, 'Get that ugly demon away!' 'No,' I replied, 'because then it will not be transformed, it will just be translocated and it will find another victim.' As mentioned earlier, this is described in the Bible: if a demon is forced to leave a victim, it hovers around for a while and then comes back to the original victim or to another entity. In doing so, it might have grown stronger or even bring another demon with it. The only way to really heal the disease is to transform the demon through love and understanding and the light of Christ. She immediately grasped and understood what I said and accepted it. I then put my hand over the demon and started to feel its pain, suffering and anger, and forgave him in the name of Christ. His fierce look became milder and he withdrew to his own sphere.

I asked the owner of the dog to keep me updated on the development of the cancer. The day after, all of the cancer seemed to have gone. The swelling was down and the lymph circulation was better. There was only some loose skin left. Some hours later the swelling started to come back, however. I then addressed the demon through my focus and intention, for I could not be present with the dog. I saw the demon before my inner eye, hurting the dog. I repeated three times to the demon: 'Light in Christ—Light in Christ—Light in Christ.' Then, after 30 minutes, I called up the dog's owner and asked how it was. She told me that all was totally normal. The dog was totally without swelling.

This shows that:

- It is important to respect demons. They also have their own life and destiny.
- Demons *want* to be transformed into the light, although many fear the transformation and try to avoid it.

- Demons are trapped in the grip of the adversaries and *want* to become free.
- When we see, hear or sense demons, we need to understand that the mere sensing of them gives us some power over them.
- Christ and Christ Consciousness have the power to free demons.

The problem of translocation of demonic pathological structures

When conventional therapists treat diseases, they are usually just translocated to other parts of the body, to other organ systems or to other animals or humans. This applies to acupuncture, zone-therapy, osteopathy, homeopathy and of course all of the treatments that have to do with massage, vitamins, minerals and food therapy. This was a recognized fact, understood by most religions and medical systems of the past.

Hering's law,[*] with which homeopaths are familiar, is presented as a law of healing, which it is not. It is the law of translocation, which describes the translocation within the body, but omits the translocation to other entities within family, friends or animals. This law can only be understood in relation to the background of 'demonology'.

How to avoid translocation, methods used within acupuncture

Example
When I visited Jaffa in Israel, I found the house where Peter visited Simon, and healed (woke from the dead) the woman Tabitha. As I sat outside the house, I was suddenly transported back in time and saw clearly how Peter did this. He

---

*Hering's Law. This law states that cure occurs:

a) *from above and downwards*. Cure progresses from the head towards the lower trunk, that is to say the head symptoms clear first. With regard to the extremities, cure spreads from shoulder to fingers, or hip to toes.

b) *from within outwards*. Cure progresses from more important organs (e.g. liver, endocrine) to less important organs (e.g. joints). That is to say, the function of vital organs are restored before those less important to life. The result of this externalization of disease is often the production of 'treatment cutaneous rash. Ards'.

c) *Appearance of symptoms in reverse chronological order*. More recent symptoms and pathology will clear before old: the disease 'back tracks' so to speak. After the more recent problems have been cleared, it is not at all uncommon for the patient to experience the transient reoccurrence of old symptoms and pathology, which then disappear within a few weeks. Hering's Law, which is also termed the Law of Cure, is the logical inverse of the way in which chronic disease progresses, both with regard to the patient himself and the ancestral history of the disease. The most important aspects of Hering's Law are, 'from within outwards' and 'in reverse chronological order'.

approached the sick/dead woman and passed her (turning his back on her). Then he turned around and watched how Lucifer and Ahriman had joined together in her death, situated in her heart region. He then pressed his finger in the tiny gap between them (they can never join totally), pressed them apart and brought Tabitha back to life. This you will find described in Acts 9:36–42. The 'turning back' is described there also.

Let us again consider the concept that to avoid translocating the disease, one had to treat with Christ Consciousness or the Middle Point.

During the crucifixion, Christ hung in the middle between two robbers, one representing luciferic crimes, the other ahrimanic crimes.

- The ahrimanic criminal mocked Jesus Christ and was condemned for eternity to the Eighth Sphere.
- The luciferic criminal begged to join Christ when he came into his own kingdom, and Jesus Christ, who has promised even Lucifer access into the heavens one day, granted the criminal man his wish.

The first time I tried to treat the Middle, and only the Anatomical Middle, I was standing beside a horse together with Dr Markus Steiner, a German colleague. Suddenly I *saw*, quite clearly, with my spiritual eyes, the ahrimanic pathological structure in the stomach area of the horse, and the luciferic pathological structure in the area of the chest. With a violent shot from a dermojet,* I then treated the exact Middle between the two, and immediately they both pulled back. According to Dr Markus Steiner, the alien entities did not entirely leave the body, but stayed in the front and the hind legs. Later I found that the structures were not supposed to leave the body completely, but to transform into the usual elemental etheric structures that exist in all bodies. The demonic part will, however, leave, either by being driven out or by being dissolved. I have seen that if I treat the Middle too violently, the demonic part does not totally go away. The Middle has to be treated with care, with a needle or with the fingers.

Since 2014, I have treated many human and veterinary patients following this method, using one needle carefully placed in the Middle. Most of them are very satisfied with the great effect of this treatment. They describe strong energies changing and streaming through the body. Often these energies stream around in the shape of a lemniscate, and usually seek out the area of the body or the process containing the demonic structure and stream into this part. The patient feels this as a strong healing effect and feels changed afterwards.

---

* A dermojet is a spring-loaded acupuncture 'gun' that can shoot a liquid into the skin of most animals and people.

Anatomically it is easy to find the Middle Point, as long as I have the ability to see with my spiritual eyes.* The Middle Point has really nothing to do with acupuncture, as I do not use any acupuncture point. I just put a needle between two areas of the body. It was more difficult to develop a method to find the Middle Point using the known acupuncture points, as acupuncture is based on duality, on yin/yang, and not the Trinity, which we have to use to find the Middle—the Christ.

The following is a technical explanation, mainly for practitioners:

I understood clearly that we could not use the five-element cycle as in acupuncture, as there is no Middle Point in the pentagram. The solution came from a colleague, Corinne Dettmer, who suggested we make two triangles out of the 'six' processes. This was of course right! I have always felt that the combination of both the heart and the pericardium within the Fire process was wrong. I had even tried to modify the five-element star to fit the six yin processes, as six individually divided functions.

I divided the heart and the pericardium, and thus created two triangles:

1. HT—KI—LV (the pulses on the left-hand wrist)
2. PC—LU—SP (the pulses on the right-hand wrist)

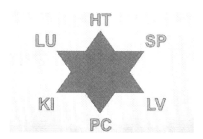

How to treat the Middle after the 6 Principle

---

* The luciferic structures are almost always proximal or cranial. The ahrimanic structures are almost always distal or caudal. As mentioned, there is also another group of pathological structures, known in ancient tradition as the azuric demons. They are said to be a special group of the ahrimanic demons and they attack the 'I' of human beings itself. They are the most dangerous of all. In olden times, the luciferic demons were the most dangerous. In our present time the ahrimanic are the most dangerous, and in future times the azuric demons will be the most dangerous. I seldom find or see these demons, so there is not much I can say about them.

- Traditionally the luciferic demons relate to the feelings, the astral forces of the body.
- Traditionally the ahrimanic demons relate to the growth forces of the body, the etheric forces.
- Traditionally the azuric demons relate to the spirit, the consciousness, the 'I' organization of the body.

In these two triangles, we have to find the middle between the excess and the deficiency.

How do we practise finding the acupuncture Middle Point or process? First, we must analyze the pulse very carefully. We must decide which pulse position is the weakest. This we must do in the twelfth layer, in the middle of the heart. When the main deficiency is found, the rest becomes easier. If the main deficiency is on the left hand (either HT, LV or KI; let us say in this example that it is LV), we must then consider the two other pulses on this same hand (either HT or KI; let us say in this example that it is KI). The Middle Point is then the remaining process, namely, in this example, HT. If the main deficiency is on the right hand, the Middle will then be either LU, SP or PC.

In treatment, one point is then needled on the meridian related to this Middle Process or Christ Process, and it is not so important which point. Use one of the command points, preferably the 'ting-point' or the source point.

Dr Vet. Markus Steiner has a slightly different procedure. He searches directly for the Middle Point, the Christ Point, and does not find the excess and the deficiency first. He feels the presence of the Christ Energy directly and uses this process as the Middle one.

Interestingly enough, this dividing or extending of the traditional Chinese five elements to six elements, inspired by my stay in Jerusalem, did not enhance the effect of the cancer treatment. In ordinary treatment of various diseases, it enhances the effect by 40%.

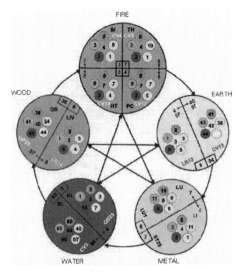

Command points

The Chinese five elements

- Fire controls Metal.
- Earth controls Water.
- Metal controls Wood.
- Water controls Fire.
- Wood controls Earth.

This method worked for 30 years, and then stopped working. After a while, I understood that I had to change the Chinese way of thinking. (They actually did know about translocation but did not care about it. It seems to me that the construction of five elements is designed to treat the excess and further translocation.)

I understood that I had to transform the whole thinking of these pre-Christian systems to a post-Christian system, based on anthroposophy. I then took the spatial relationship of the seven planets and related them to the seven processes that they represent, and this resulted in the seven-star, as below:

The Anthroposophic seven elements

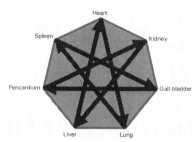

Body processes relating to space

- Heart controls Lung.
- Kidney controls Liver.
- Gall-bladder controls Pericardium.
- Lung controls Spleen.
- Liver controls Heart.
- Pericardium controls Kidney.
- Spleen controls Gall-bladder.

This worked for three years, and then stopped working. I then related the seven processes of the body also to time, as time *protects* the spiritual from the adversaries, as explained earlier.

Then I then came up with the following figure:

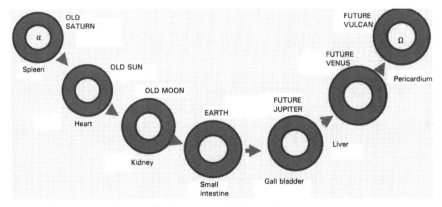

Body processes relating to time

The Anthroposophic seven time-elements

- Spleen controls Pericardium and vice versa.
- Heart controls Liver and vice versa.
- Kidney controls Gall-bladder and vice versa.
- Lung control Lungs and vice versa.

This works for now.

In treating cancer, I then decided to use two needles. One relating to control of space, and one relating to the control of time. And *voilà*, once again the treatment worked!

Now we will analyze how and why the adversaries wanted to stop and tried to stop the effect of the cancer therapy. This will shed a lot of light on the working of demons and the adversaries in general.

How demons can defend themselves through translocation or combined and enforced strength when seen, threatened or attacked therapeutically

A description of the causes of cancer, the explosion of this disease today, why it is so difficult to heal and my (very) personal experiences in treating cancer.

All our diseases are caused by, or effectuated by, the cooperation of ahrimanic (the doppelgänger) and luciferic demons inhabiting our bodies.

In most diseases there is a certain and individual distance between the two kinds of demons. The stronger and less diseased the specific person or patient is, the further the two types of demons are separated. In healthy, young persons, they may be 20 cm apart; in healthy horses, they are 80 cm apart.

In cancer, the cooperation of these demons is quite special, as they have come closer together; there is almost no distance between them.

This lack of distance between the ahrimanic and the luciferic demons makes it very difficult to heal as they have joined forces. It is much easier for them to stay put or, if they have to translocate, this is also quite a problem for them. This is the curse of our present times, resulting in the explosion of cancer that we see rising in all countries of the world.

Moreover, the times that we are living in make it easier for demons to unite in the way described, and as such promote the cooperation of luciferic and ahrimanic forces. Our very time-spirit, or rather lack of time-spirit, brings them closer together, closer than ever before. So, what is it in our modern mentality and the spiritual composition of the human soul today that makes this happen, this enhanced 'friendship' between Ahriman and Lucifer?

The love of our material possessions and the lack of humility and belief in the spiritual world opens us to Ahriman. Combined with greed and lust for money and hatred towards the spiritual world, which opens us to Lucifer, this allows for the close cooperation and entrance of both the adversaries. This is relevant for the civilization at large, but not necessarily for individuals.

In 1983, I realized that cancer had to be treated totally differently from all other diseases. Most diseases can be treated by addressing one of the two demons: either by weakening or opposing the luciferic demon (excessive and symptomatic treatment) or by weakening or opposing the ahrimanic demon (deficient treatment). Both these methods are more or less symptomatic, often just translocating the pathology to other places or to other entities, humans or animals.

The method of weakening (or, actually, translocating) the ahrimanic demon was achieved through strengthening the deficient organ-function. This pushed out the ahrimanic demon, and thereby enhanced control over the luciferic demon. This was achieved through what I have described, in numerous articles and in my book on alternative veterinary medicine, as 'controlling' treatment.

In 1984, I first applied the 'controlling' treatment method on a dachshund. The dog had mammary cancer (multiple tumours along the nipple line) and had begun to develop dyspnea (heavy breathing). It probably had several lung metastases. With acupuncture, I treated the point labeled as LV03 (liver 3), which strengthens the liver organ and as such weakens the 'grip' of the ahrimanic demon on the liver, thus strengthening the control of the luciferic demon relating to the mammary glands. In a few weeks, the tumours had almost completely disappeared. The dog died several years later from a kidney deficiency.

In 1995, for the first time, I treated a horse using the same method. The horse had been diagnosed with *equine sarcoid*, a kind of horse cancer. The result was very promising; the sarcoid disappeared within six weeks, and this case was published in the journal of the Norwegian Veterinary Society, *Norsk Veterinærtidsskrift*.

Since 1984, I have treated more than a thousand patients suffering from all kinds of cancer, both animals and humans. The results have been especially good in mammary cancer (85%), also in Melan sarcoma (80%). Results in lymphosarcoma and brain cancer have been moderately good (70%). However, my results in liver cancer and pancreatic cancer were mediocre; the healing rate being 'only' 60% in the few patients I have treated.

As I started to 'see' the disease-bringing demons more and more with my spiritual eyes, I understood increasingly the necessity of hindering the described translocation. This was done by and through the understanding of Christ, the Middle Point and the importance of not fighting the adversaries directly, but rather to transform them in love, as described in my book, *Sevenfold Way to Therapy*.

In 2014, I then stared to experiment with both methods, especially within cancer treatment. Then something quite unexpected happened. In cancer therapy, the controlling treatment had worked very well for me for exactly 30 years. Then, in the period of Spring 2014, as I tried to hinder the demons from translocating, it gradually ceased to work, or at least the effect lessened considerably. There was still an effect: the growth of the tumours decreased, but the real *healing* seen before was lost.

Five of my closest students reported the same; the cancer treatment method gradually ceased working in the early part of 2014, even if both my students and I applied solely the well-proven protocol (i.e. did not try to hinder the translocation through applying the Middle Point). The method even ceased to work for my students who were unaware of my experiments in trying to hinder the translocation. (This did not happen to those of my students that had learned the method through reading my articles; only to those who had learned it directly from me.)

It was very confusing for me. What was going on? Why did this happen? I did not tell anybody of this change in my results, as initially I did not believe it, especially as the treatment of all other diseases, both through the controlling method and through the Middle Point, continued to work very well—even better after I introduced the Middle Point therapy.

The results after using the Middle Point method were actually much better than the results I had had before. It was only in cancer treatment that I could observe this decrease in effect.

At first, I thought it was just due to a period of less successful results, occurring by chance, and that the good results would reappear, but they did not. They have now been lost for some two-and-a-half years.

We are thus left with some deep questions:

1. Why did the effect of both the Controlling Method and the Middle Point Method change or totally cease when I started to try to hinder the translocation (or was it some other event in 2013 and 2014 that caused this change)?
2. Why did the effect of the Controlling Method and the Midpoint Method cease for most of my 'personal' students but not for my distant students?

I will try to give some possible answers, although I do not know the answer for sure:

a. The demons will not transform. In ordinary diseases, they were not strong enough to withstand the Middle Point, but the demons that have joined forces in cancer had the strength to do so.
b. My ability to 'see' the demons brought about a possibility for the strongest demons, especially in diseases where the luciferic and the ahrimanic demons have joined forces, to change or translocate, as described in quantum physics (when an elemental particle is 'seen', it changes radically).
c. I accepted that certain people could be allowed to earn money by using my method. This invited in Mammon, a very strong, ahrimanic demon.
d. The effect stopped for my students because we are 'entangled', as also described in quantum physics. This entanglement was only with my personal students, not the ones that I had never met.
e. It has to do with some changes in the world,* that enables the strongest demons to endure, but not the weaker ones.

---

* In this period, the wall between 'our' world and the ahrimanic and luciferic world(s) was shattered by the Large Hadron Collider in CERN, Switzerland. The Large Hadron Collider (LHC) is the world's largest and most powerful particle accelerator. It first started up on 10 September 2008, and remains the latest addition to CERN's accelerator complex. The LHC consists of a 27-kilometre ring of superconducting magnets with a number of accelerating structures to boost the energy of the particles along the way.

f. I completed my personal karma, as described in my book, *The Forgotten Mysteries of Atlantis*, and this karma included the work I have done as a therapist and teacher in pulse-diagnosis.

Lately, I have started to see another explanation, found in quantum physics. I have earlier argued that the laws in quantum physics are the same as the laws governing the elemental or spiritual worlds. There are two important laws in quantum physics:

1. The uncertainty principle,[*] proposed by Werner Heisenberg.
2. The law of entanglement.[†]

These two laws actually describe all the amazing changes I have observed within my cancer therapy.

---

[*] The uncertainty principle is one of the most famous (and probably most misunderstood) ideas in physics. It tells us that there is a 'fuzziness' in nature, a fundamental limit to what we can know about the behaviour of quantum particles and, therefore, the smallest scales of nature. Of these scales, the most we can hope for is to calculate probabilities for where things are and how they will behave. Unlike Isaac Newton's clockwork universe, where everything follows clear-cut laws on how to move and prediction is easy if you know the starting conditions, the uncertainty principle enshrines a level of fuzziness into quantum theory. Werner Heisenberg's simple idea tells us why atoms don't implode, how the sun manages to shine and, strangely, that the vacuum of space is not actually empty. An early incarnation of the uncertainty principle appeared in a 1927 paper by Heisenberg, a German physicist who was working at Niels Bohr's institute in Copenhagen at the time, titled 'On the Perceptual Content of Quantum Theoretical Kinematics and Mechanics'. The more familiar form of the equation came a few years later, when he had further refined his thoughts in subsequent lectures and papers.

[†] Quantum entanglement is a physical phenomenon that occurs when pairs or groups of particles are generated or interact in ways such that the quantum state of each particle cannot be described independently of the others, even when the particles are separated by a large distance—instead, a quantum state must be described for the system as a whole. Measurements of physical properties such as position, momentum, spin and polarization, performed on entangled particles, are found to be appropriately correlated. For example, if a pair of particles are generated in such a way that their total spin is known to be zero, and one particle is found to have clockwise spin on a certain axis, the spin of the other particle, measured on the same axis, will be found to be counterclockwise, as to be expected due to their entanglement. However, this behaviour gives rise to paradoxical effects: any measurement of a property of a particle can be seen as acting on that particle (e.g., by collapsing a number of superposed states) and will change the original quantum property by some unknown amount, and in the case of entangled particles such a measurement will be on the entangled system as a whole. It thus appears that one particle of an entangled pair 'knows' what measurement has been performed on the other, and with what outcome, even though there is no known means for such information to be communicated between the particles, which at the time of measurement may be separated by arbitrarily large distances.

When I started to 'see' the elementals (in physics called the elementary particles), they changed and were able to avoid me. As well as this, I am 'entangled' with most of my students, so that the same will happen to them. Additionally, we may ponder why the spreading of knowledge of this method has been effectively stopped every time the possibility has arisen to officially prove the efficiency of the method.[*]

My personal thoughts to these questions are as follows: In the beginning of 2014, I began to understand the phenomenon of translocation and how it could be hindered. I changed my protocol of therapy so that the demons would not just translocate but were also faced with transformation. Apparently, it is not obvious that they want to change into light.[†] I had to use will to transform the demons of cancer, although in other diseases love was sufficient.

I now understand that the demons try to defend themselves, to survive as demons, even if they actually want to be transformed. Why do they have to defend themselves? Is it because I started to become too strong or too dangerous for them, due to my new way of treating diseases, together with my 'new' connection to Christ? Is it because I 'saw' them with my spiritual eyes, and thus enabled them to escape? Is it that the finishing of my 40,000-year-old karma had come to an end? Is it that Mammon had been allowed to 'have a finger' within this project? Or, is it a combination of these factors?

Before, I always treated either the excess or the deficiency. Then, the demons could just translocate; it was not so 'dangerous' for them.

But when I realized this translocation more and more and started to treat the Middle Point to change the demons, to dissolve them into the light, they tried to avoid my treatment. They tried to find ways of withstanding the treatment. In 'normal' diseases, the demons cannot

---

[*] Described in the book, *Does the Riddle of Cancer Have a Solution?* by Finn Thoreson, CreateSpace, 2016.

[†] Here I was faced with an enigma. In 'ordinary' diseases, my impression is that the demons want to change into light. In cancer, this is different. Here, it seems that the demons try to avoid such a transformation. This phenomenon can also be seen in how the cancer demons relate to sunlight. Several investigations show that *sitting* too much in the sun can create cancer; other retrospective investigations show that people that *work* in the sun have less cancer. This seems to be a contradiction. A possible answer to this contradiction is based upon how the etheric energy or body relates to the will, to working or not working. This has to do with the relationship between the moving etheric, in which the will is present, and the stationary etheric, in which the *will* is not present. If the will is absent, then the conjunction of the ahrimanic and the luciferic demons is facilitated, and this can lead to cancer. If the will of the demons is not counteracted by the will of the human being, the will of the demonic powers can create cancer.

avoid the transforming treatment, but in cancer, the close cooperation of the luciferic and the ahrimanic demons leads to greater strength, and they are thus able to avoid the transformation.

A Belgian colleague wrote me the following message, after I had asked several colleagues if they had noticed some change in the effect in cancer treatment during the last two years. This colleague had no knowledge of or belief in demons. However, he wrote the following:

> As far as your question on cancer treatment is concerned my observations are the following: I do not remember if things changed two years ago, but I have noticed a general difference in reaction of patients. Where the approach seemed to be simple, direct and effective before, it seems as if it is different now. I can refer to stomach cancer in a Labrador dog ten years ago as an example. One needle once a month reduced the tumour from the size of a basketball to a ping-pong ball. It stayed in this state until the dog died two years later. Testing before each treatment revealed the same meridian/organ complex was involved and as a consequence the same acupuncture point was needled at each session. I noticed that it is not so anymore. Maybe it is to do with the location of tumours that makes a difference, or maybe it is to do with myself, but what I notice is that the tumour/cancer seems to try to 'escape' the treatment protocol. For instance, last September I started to treat a cat with an osteosarcoma initiating in St01 (acupuncture point) right side. Testing before treatment involved Stomach Meridian/organ complex only. The owner is a colleague/friend and did not want to wait one month for the next session, so I saw the cat a week later for a check-up. This time the tumour seemed the same in shape and location, however ... it showed another meridian involved when testing before treatment. I found a reaction in GB (Meridian) now and nothing in St (Meridian) anymore. The tumour tried to 'escape' the Stomach Meridian and move to the GB01 (acupuncture point) position, so treatment needed an adaptation of strategy. During the last session last week, it shifted to SI (Meridian). I have seen this on several other occasions too for some time now, and even if the tumours stay under control, it seems to me that the reaction to treatment is not in the same straightforward way as it has been for all the previous years. I do not know what your observations are and why you send out the question, but I hope that my observations can be of some help to you.

It is as if he is describing demons ...

If my assessment is correct and this change is connected to my 'seeing' and knowledge of the cancer-causing demons and my use of the Middle

Point enabling me to transform them, then how could this change the behaviour of the demons in Belgium? On the other hand, one could ask, why should it not? Is this 'entanglement', as described in quantum physics? Can it be that my knowledge will interfere with all my students? So, deep questions . . .

A good doctor friend of mine from Stockholm suggested the following:

> Today, 25% of the population will die from cancer due to the way we live our lives, allowing Ahriman and Lucifer to join in our bodies. We let love and greed for money along with the lack of religious humility open us up to both the adversaries. This will create cancer.
>
> The cancer itself is thus the healing of this condition. The disease, as all other diseases, is a symptom and a healing for a deeper and spiritual unbalance.
>
> I can still heal those with whom I have a personal karma. That is in my destiny. However, if my methods should be used on a much larger scale, it would not heal the deeper cause of the disease itself, which is the combination of greed and atheism, opening up to the adversaries. This must be addressed first and worked upon in a spiritual way. Before this is addressed, the treatment of cancer will stop working. First, we must address the attack of the adversaries, otherwise we will not be able to heal cancer patients, except those with whom we still have a personal karma.

Another colleague commented in the following way (on 2 July 2016):

> The Middle Point is the reason of any treatment done with mistletoe: Viscum Album, Iscusin, Iscador, all made by Wala. Of course, I have the tendency of recommending Wala medicaments. They are manufactured according to Rudolf Steiner's indications in order to increase the immunological system—and in humans, all of us have an 'I'; the main point of any treatment is to strengthen Christ's forces.
>
> Often, the point is not to live without the disease, nor is it to suffer unbearably with the disease but to learn how to live with the disease and handle it. Anyway, Steiner was very clear that all researches on Viscum had to happen in a deep way as, according to him, by using Viscum the need for surgery due to cancer would disappear.
>
> According to a few medical doctor friends of mine, this will never happen. There is not enough money to run researches under anthroposophical guidance, and the allopathic labs dominate the health research field in such a way that suffocates all forms of healing outside

their approval. The more they control health decisions in all directions (WHO, state controls of medicaments and diseases), the more distant are all possibilities to raise enough money to run good research with good results that are accessible to all health communities and to the population in general. Unfortunately, this is the hard reality. There is some research happening now but I have personal reasons to believe it will always represent loss and the institutionalised power is not open to loss.

Thank you, your feedback is just a marvellous fresh stream of water. If you are 63-years-old or more, I dare to say your karma has been overcome and unless you create a new stream of treatment, your 'I' will not anymore be the donor of healing forces or the carrier—as you also clearly see. It is necessary to create a new and even more innovative way to heal.

A colleague from Mexico wrote me this email:

Dear Are, In the beginning, after you taught me the method, my results were great. Almost all cancers were healed. Then, about two years ago, I started to experience mixed results, not always the best ones (remission).

This improved a little when I selected the acupoint by pulse resonance (according to Nogier) on the corresponding carpal or tarsal areas, as you have described in your book. But after a while the results started to get worse again. I am curious about your personal experiences. I send you greetings from rainy Mexico City.

A colleague from Germany wrote me this email:

Dear Are, Thank you for your paper. In 2014, we discussed a lot about the ahrimanic and luciferic in the pulse. New things arose to our consciousness. We cannot neglect this in our therapies. The few cancer patients I treated, I now can only treat by searching the positive, the balanced process in the patient himself and amplifying this Christ energy inside the patient. It is only giving a sign to the patient where the healing is 'stored' in his 'body'. Make him aware of the 'good energy'. Not fighting demons, just amplifying love. Love is the only way to cure, I guess. Will ask doctors I meet what they observed. Love M.

At this stage, I find it important to emphasize that the effect of cancer treatment, when based on a spiritual foundation, is not at all stable or expected to be stable. I have seen through my life that the effect varies with several factors, of which the most important are:

1. The geographical location of both the therapist and the patient.
2. The directions of the mountains, if they are situated east-west or north-south.
3. The rigidity of the etheric body of the patient.
4. How much the patient has meditated.
5. The knowledge of the therapist, especially spiritual knowledge of the demonic causes of the disease.
6. The karma of both the therapist and the patient.
7. The karma or strength of the disease itself, that is, of the demon(s) causing the disease.
8. The love and empathy between the therapist and the patient.

All of these factors influence the ability of the demons to resist treatment.

Examples

1. *The personal doctor of the Dalai Lama had excellent results with his patients back home in Tibet. In Norway, to my knowledge, he had no results at all with his Norwegian patients (the Himalayan and Norwegian mountains are not parallel, but oppositely situated, see point 2 above).*
2. *I had no results at all for several years when treating Herpes Zoster (Shingles). After reading a lecture by Rudolf Steiner on the spiritual causes and origins of this disease, I had excellent results for exactly three years, after which time I had no results again.*
3. *When treating cancer with my 'five-star control method', I had remarkably better results in treating patients from Switzerland than patients from Norway (see point 1).*
4. *I had excellent results in treating breast-cancer in both dogs and humans from 1984 to 2014. Then the positive results disappeared or changed markedly in 'favour' of the demons.*
5. *Rudolf Steiner reported that the effect that Dr Wilhelm Heinrich Schüssler had with his cell salts would only last some years, after which the effects would disappear. To my knowledge, Steiner did not say why this was so or why it would happen in such a way.*[*]

After thinking through all these points, I decided to change my treatment. My daughter, Eve Thoresen, gave me an idea, which led to the first change. She said, 'Why not stop the demon from escaping before you do the treatment?'

I then introduced the 'Middle Point with Christ Consciousness',

---

[*] See Rudolf Steiner, *Introducing Anthroposophical Medicine*, lecture of 31 March 1920, Dornach (SteinerBooks USA, 2010).

restricted therapy. This therapy is about stopping the demons from disappearing, holding them fast so to speak, by means of words, needles or by other methods, and then treating the disease either by the Controlling Method or by the Middle Point. I am currently evaluating the effect of this method, but the results have not yet been very good.

Then another train of thought came to my mind. Could the pathological cooperation of the Yin and the Yang elementals be traced to an unhealthy relationship between men and women in society as a whole? Can we understand the development of cancer as a symptom, on a deeper level, of a flawed cooperation between masculine and feminine—Jesus and Christ—Jesus and Mary Magdalene—Yin and Yang—Ahriman and Lucifer—man not understanding woman ... and vice versa, of course. Could this be seen in the case of a cell transmuting into cancer cells? Is there a lack of understanding between the growth (feminine) and the control of the growth (masculine)? Well, of course there is!

The balancing of the negative aspect of the masculine, which is the ahrimanic, and the negative aspect of the feminine, which is the luciferic, can only be balanced through the Middle.

Man not understanding woman and woman not understanding man causes most disease today. In this lack of communication, the demonic beings of Lucifer and Ahriman can enter and create cancer. This concept of man not understanding woman and vice versa is a social event, it is down to society as a whole.

Then something unexpected happened. By the help of destiny, I lectured in upstate New York and was also going to treat the participants of the course. I decided to treat according to the anatomical midpoint, the Christ point. On the evening of 5 November, 2016, 25 participants lay on the floor, and I treated them all at the individual midpoint between Lucifer and Ahriman. The work with the needle took 20 minutes. I then sat back to watch.

The needle that was placed in the stomach, between the adversaries, seemed to activate this area of 'free' etheric force, not dominated by Ahriman or Lucifer. This area became activated, became rhythmic and oscillating. After some time, the ahrimanic demons became more light-filled, started to float up from the participants and circled around and over the whole group. The circling became more and more luminous, going upwards in a maelstrom. In the Light, the face of an angel appeared (or an archangel). One of the participants saw the being of Michael. I went into the middle of the vortex and had a divine feeling.

The needling of the Middle Point caused an oscillation in the etheric body, just between the ahrimanic and the luciferic pathological structures.

This oscillation in the different patients started to make a sympathetic resonance between the different members of the group. The resonance multiplied the strength of the treatment to a very high degree, so that the whole group was drawn into the effect of the treatment, even in those where the ahrimanic and the luciferic demons were tightly bound together, as they are in cancer. What I could not have done in such patients individually was achieved through the whole group.

The effect in a group was totally different to treating individuals. This understanding struck me like a light from heaven. Of course, the cooperation of the demons had made them strong—so strong that they could withstand the individual patient and treatment. However, they could not withstand the power of the group. The cooperation of the good in each and every one of the patients was then able to transform the evil into the light.

This described effect was stronger in the dawn and the dusk, as etheric forces are always stronger at these times. Patients lying east-west also felt a stronger effect than those lying north-south. I have always had a better result in treating cancer in patients coming from areas of the world where the mountains were directed east-west (Alps, Himalayas) than those coming from areas where the mountains are directed north-south (Norway, USA).

The difference observed in group therapy made me realize that the adversaries try to push spiritual or energetic medicine into their own regions by separating people.

The restricting method that I tried first was overly based in conventional thinking, as 'one therapist and one patient'. The ahrimanic forces try to overtake the realm of healing methods and the healing process by individualizing each treatment, as is so much talked about today in modern medicine; specialized and individual treatment through the immune system. In this way, the adversaries can avoid the treatment; they can even gain power and energy through such a method.

This is known by the darker brotherhoods, where black magic is performed, based on stealing etheric energy for single individuals through different kinds of treatments, procedures or rituals. In my life I have met with two such groups: the historical Thule Society in Germany and a certain contemporary occult organization in Italy.

I visited the Thule Society in Germany some years ago. They were organizing and operating a quite large school in Scandinavia where the alternative, energetic healing arts were taught, like acupuncture, zone-therapy and homeopathy. I asked one of the professors in this school for permission to visit him in Germany, which was granted. On the first day of the visit, I realized that most of the patients at his clinic were old or younger Nazis, and I became a little frightened.

However, the most interesting and frightening event happened on the last day of the visit. The professor I was visiting invited me to a private dinner at his house. On arriving, I was faced with a huge painting of Christ on the cross, hanging upside down. During the dinner, I saw with my spiritual eyes that a certain small photograph on the wall pulsated negative energy towards the professor. As I told him this, he turned the picture and in the next second, he fainted. I quickly tried to revive him.

After some time, he woke up, and as he was convinced that I had saved his life he then told me the true story of the activity of the Thule Society. This group were masters in the 'art' of black magic, and for every healing their students did, a certain part of the energy, or let us rather say the demons that were translocated, were used by the leaders of this group for their own dark purposes.

Many years later, the Italian organization came to Norway to build special stone labyrinths. They were quite open regarding the fact that all who went into these labyrinths would transfer energy or elementals to the 'Selfic' temple-room in Northern Italy, to be used by their leaders in their activities, whatever they may be.

This is one of the many ways that the adversaries try to gain control over the etheric forces and powers in their fight against all that is good. Another way is for the ahrimanic forces, in addition to individualizing the treatment, is to mechanize it in order to maintain control, as machines are under their dominion. This can be fought or counteracted by placing Christ in the middle of a group of human patients. The group therapy based on the Christ Middle Point showed me that this might be the right way to go: 'Where two or three are gathered in my name, there I am in the midst of them.'

According to Rudolf Steiner, we will become increasingly infused with technology, and this will be utilized by the adversaries to gain access and control over the whole of human evolution. By using the social element of group treatment combined with the absence of machines, using only one single needle in the healthiest point of the body, namely the Christ Point, we can advance in preventing the disastrous cooperation between Lucifer and Ahriman that creates the epidemic wave of cancer we see today. Further, we can in this way turn the whole medical sphere towards the spiritual conception of the world.

The exact Middle Point, where Lucifer and Ahriman join their hands, can be seen in the wooden artwork made by Rudolf Steiner, called 'The Representative of Humanity'. The hands of Lucifer and Ahriman join just below the heart of Christ.

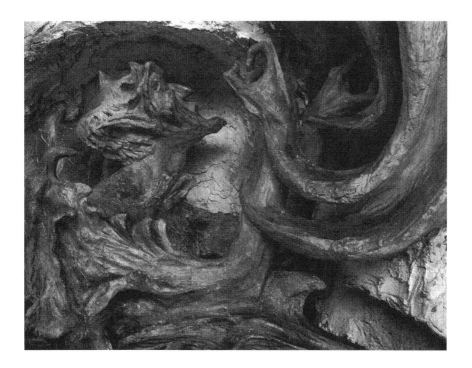

The importance of Archangel Michael's fight against demons

As described previously, demons do not want to meet the Archangel Michael,* who stands on the side of Christ, who is the highest commander of all the legions of angels in their fight against the demonic hordes.

There are many old stories and an extensive literature on how Michael, the spiritual being of the rank of archangeloi, leads the legions of angels and good forces in the great battle against the legions of Ahriman and Lucifer. Here I will share what my friends and I have experienced, and then will try to draw the conclusion of how to fight, and hopefully how to win, this existential battle.

Example 1
One of my friends was attacked in the house of a Lodge based in London that was dealing with black magic. Ironically, this lodge was called 'White Lodge'. He was invited into one of their flats and left there to wait. After a short while, a statue of Buddha started to pulsate energy towards him that became stronger and stronger. Understanding that he was in danger, he made the almost fatal decision to show

---

* Michael ('Who is like unto God') is an archangel in Judaism, Christianity and Islam.

that he too had some strength. One of his abilities was to perform psychokinesis (moving physical items by will), and he set one of the ceiling-lights in motion. Immediately, the pulsations from the Buddha figure became stronger. After a short while, he was overpowered and fell to the floor. As he understood that death might occur, he gave up all resistance and asked Jesus Christ and Michael for help. Immediately the pulsating stopped, and he was free to walk away.

Example 2

Another friend was walking in the forest close to Trondheim, Middle Norway, just west of the town. Suddenly he was attacked by an entity that he was unable to see with his eyes. The fight lasted for 30 minutes and the enemy became stronger and stronger the more my friend fought back. Suddenly my friend relaxed, giving up all resistance, asking Jesus Christ and Michael for help. As soon as this happened, the enemy disappeared.

Both thought that they possessed enough strength to fight the demonic entity. Both were close to being killed when they realized that the more they fought the demon, the more it sucked strength and power from them. That is one of the secrets of the Dark Forces; they have no power of their own. They can only feed on the fright and resistance that they initiate. In the fight against evil powers, we need both to resist fighting them and to ask for help from Michael or from Christ.

Example 3

In this extract from my book, The Forgotten Mysteries of Atlantis, *I speak about my own experiences in the third person:*

> ... he met three dangerous and extremely strong demons. They were huge and fierce ... he saw and understood that they had been with him for 25,000 years. They had been with him in all his destructive ways of being, in all his ill deeds. He had created them in his incarnation as an Oracle, created or attracted them from another dimension from another realm of existence. These demons had been with him throughout his many lives, helped him in his greed for power, in his black deeds, in his manipulations of others, in his misuse of all that he could misuse. 'What do you want with us?' they shouted at him. Their voices felt like thunder. 'I want us, both you and me, to be free,' he answered calmly. 'We have followed the Black Path together long enough. Now the time has come to change. The time has come to end this. Now the time has come to choose the White Path. Now the time has come to make all the old, black karma into good karma. Now it is time to refrain from power.' He was quite amazed with

himself, how he could say all this in front of such terrible and frightening creatures. He understood that he had to fight the demons. He had to fight them with the mental projection of his earthly body; he had to fight them with the whole of himself because the memories and actions committed in previous ages and past incarnations were still imprinted in his current physical body. Now he had to use his 'muscles and arms' in this present incarnation to fight them, even though he knew that this was only an illusion, for there are no actual muscles and arms in the spiritual world. Still, he had to fight as if he were in the physical world (much like in the film *The Matrix*). The fight started and went on for a considerable time. He became more and more tired. He could not rest for one moment or else the demons would get the upper hand. They were impossible to get through. Suddenly he felt despair, but this despair brought him salvation ... He understood that strength and power could not bring him victory. He understood that Love was the only way ... He called out for Christ, the love and light of Christ, and in the same instant the demons were noticeably weakened. This was a very important moment, but he did not understand or conceive the full importance of his cry until later, when he fully realized the importance of the Christ for the whole development of the earth, until the end of all time. He now had to concentrate all his strength on conquering the demons. The demons showed definite signs of weakening, and the darkness faded. He suddenly felt a glimmer of hope. Faith entered his spirit, victory approached. After a final effort, he really managed to 'go through' them, straight through ... and into the light.

Example 4

A group of women living in Middle Europe had been using mediumship and channelling to guide them in their lives and to reveal their past lives (which of course were glorious!), and even to help choose husbands and to decide whether to divorce.

A close friend of mine was invited to speak to this group. As he was very preoccupied with the work of the Archangel Michael, who is opposed and hostile to demons, he chose to talk on this subject. On his journey to the place of the lecture, he was severely afflicted by both toothache and a headache, a combination that he had never experienced before. He almost cancelled the lecture but decided to carry on.

It was clear that the demons abiding with this group of women feared the knowledge of Michael and wanted to stop my friend from teaching them about this universal force. My friend later told me how surprised he was that such a spiritual group of women had never before heard about Michael.

I tried to help their leader see the backward path she and her group were on, but little helped. Interestingly enough, this group also denied the importance of the will. According to Rudolf Steiner, the will and the transformation of the will is of crucial importance for the future of Christianity.

Example 5

In the winter of 2016/17, I went on holiday to India. My wife and I had travelled from Oslo to Abu-Dhabi and had two days' rest there. During that stay, we went out into the desert and experienced the feeling of desolation to be found there. I stood for a while by myself and watched the wide expanses of the Arabian Desert. A movement in the distance caught my attention, and I looked more carefully. At a certain distance I saw a group of jinn, the demons of the desert. They looked very different from all other elementary beings I had seen before. The Norwegian elemental beings, like Nisser, Dverger and even trolls, looked like polite schoolboys compared to jinn. They looked fierce, had long teeth—as sharp as a tiger—and had a very bloodthirsty look in their bloodshot eyes. I felt a certain fear as I watched them. Then one of these jinn, possibly their leader, caught my eye as I was studying them. The jinn saw that I saw them, and the whole group turned and rushed aggressively towards me.

The leader of the jinn stopped just in front of me and pierced me with his fierce eyes. He tried to enter me, and I, who was used to elemental beings and how to keep them at a distance, had difficulties. The strength of this elemental being was remarkable. He pressed on towards me and tried to get into my soul. Then I made the sign of Michael, as taught by Rudolf Steiner, and in a second the demon was rendered unable to fight. The whole group turned away and rushed further into and through the desert.

Later at the hotel, when I asked the local Arabs about the jinn, many of them had seen these creatures, and they were amazed that a white foreigner, even a Christian, had been able to see them.

An example of how not everything is as it appears to be in terms of demons and folklore

In May 2017, I gave a course in the outskirts of Bisperode, a small village close to Hameln in the middle of Germany. During my stay, I met two 'werewolves'. All the inhabitants of Bisperode know about one of them, the one closest to the village, bound to the small graveyard situated there. There is even an information notice informing tourists about the existence of the werewolf.

I happened to pass this graveyard when I was riding in the surrounding forests of Bisperode, and while doing so I saw the werewolf. It (she) looked terrible but not dangerous. All the time, she was looking out beyond the fence of the cemetery, as if

❾ Der Werwolf im Hopfen-hofe

Im Hopfenhofe, da, wo seit 1840 der neue Bis-peröder Kirchhof liegt, ging zu mitternächtlicher Stunde ein Werwolf um. Das war ein verzauber-ter Mensch, der in ein Wolfsfell schlüpfte und nun die Eigenschaften eines Wolfes annahm. Am Luderplatze im Hopfenhöfe fraß er sich voll und erschreckte viele Menschen. Mancher übel verleumdete Mensch kam in alter Zeit aber auch leicht in den Verdacht, ein Werwolf zu sein, und wurde dann scheu gemieden und gefürchtet.

searching for something. I rode further along the country roads towards the forest. Dark clouds gathered around the horse and me and soon, after some thunder, rain and hail broke out. Close to the forest, about a thousand metres away from the graveyard, I spotted another werewolf, this one even bigger, stronger and more fierce-looking than the first one. This second one was obviously male. He also appeared to be looking for something.

I continued riding along the edge of the forest and contemplated the existence of werewolves: They are stronger during full moon, they run after virgins, they ... Suddenly the connection between the two werewolves emerged in my consciousness. What if the two beasts belonged together? An understanding of the problem emerged in my mind. What if they had once been lovers? Perhaps their families had opposed the relationship and he was killed in the forest. What if she killed herself and was buried at the graveyard, and they had looked for each other ever since?

I rode back to the graveyard and addressed the female werewolf. I told her that her lover was waiting in the forest and I pointed in the right direction. Immediately, she brightened and ran in the direction I had pointed. In a few minutes, the whole area felt lighter, the hail stopped and joy could be felt. The two lovers had found each other. Then something strange happened: my glasses, which were only six months old, fell apart. I have no explanation for this phenomenon.

A summary of how to use thinking, feeling and will in the medical treatment of patients

A description of the practical use of the spiritual soul forces in healing and their relation to the middle, the Christ

In several places in this book, I have described the dividing of the three soul forces; how the single and separated forces are experienced and how they can be used singly or in combination, especially in diagnosing and treating sick and demonically-influenced patients. Here I will give a short and systematic description of this:

Thinking must be used in the initial stage of the diagnosis of any patient, whether animal or man. We must ask about the disease, make our observations and think through how we will perform the whole operation. Is surgery needed, is the horse dangerous, can the dog bite us, do we need any medications? and so on.

Then we proceed to the separation of Thinking, Feeling and Will, as described earlier in this book. When we have reached an acceptable state of mind, we will go into feeling.

Feeling is situated mainly in the heart, or at least this organ is what we use in diagnosing the patient correctly. We leave the thinking and will behind and go totally into our own heart, all the way to the twelfth layer, to the middle of the heart. We then imagine a tunnel from our heart to the heart of the patient. This tunnel transverses all twelve layers of the body, right the way into the centre of the heart itself. Here, in the twelfth layer, we start to diagnose.

Personally, I use pulse diagnosis to go through all the different processes of the body, both in the present time and in the past, but all modalities of spiritual diagnosis may be used. Imagination, Inspiration, Intuition, the pendulum, kinesiology, or any method that may give you the information you need. We go into the processes of the forefathers and foremothers, investigate the different physical, mental or spiritual traumas, and we hold all this information in our mind. In keeping this information in mind, we have to combine thinking with feeling.

When we have decided with our thinking how to treat this disease, we again leave both the thinking and the feeling behind, and go into the will powers of the universe, which are to be found in the earth itself.

The *Will* forces must be used in the therapeutic part of the procedure. The focus of the therapist will then be in his limbs, his feet or even in the earth itself beneath his feet. From this area, the force of will is awakened, and this force will then stream up through the body. The path this force takes is often along the spine, described in old traditions as the 'Kundalini' force.

I myself often experience this streaming up through the body as a dance between two snakes, one white and one black. This force must then enter the heart, mingle with the feeling, with compassion, and love for the patient, in fact for the whole of humanity. This mingling often results in a feeling of cosmic divine love, inhabiting the centre of the heart. From this centre in the heart, the healing force, now totally cleansed from any egoistic wish or intent, streams over into the patient. Here, directed by intentional thought that streams down from the head, the healing force works in the body by diminishing the power of the demons. If this force is directed against the ahrimanic demon, the healing of the organic structures will begin. If it is directed against the luciferic demon, the pain and unpleasantness will diminish. If it is directed to the Middle, the Christ Point or the Christ-filled gap between the two demons, both demons will pull back and start to dissolve or transform.

How to use thinking, feeling and will during different kinds of treatment

There are three ways to treat a disease:

- *Treat the excess*, i.e., treat the symptoms, i.e. the luciferic demon. Then we should use our thinking, the head, the 'white light' and the rhythms of the head.
- *Treat the deficiency*, i.e., the ahrimanic demon that is the cause of the excess. Then we should activate our Will, our digestive system and our earthly, dark rhythmic energy.
- *Treat the Middle Point* with Christ Consciousness, the force of dissolving both the luciferic and ahrimanic demons. Then we should activate or use only our feeling; our love, our heart, our sunlight, our Christ. Only here can we be sure that the noxious structures, the demons, are not translocated. That is truly what is meant by treating with Christ Consciousness.

Cranio-Sacral Therapy is defined as treating through the fine pulsation of the cerebrospinal fluid. This is, of course, a crude and inaccurate material description of several deep and strong spiritual rhythms of breathing. All living beings breathe spiritually, and we may find this spiritual rhythm in the etheric body (three to six rhythms per minute), in the astral body (one rhythm in ten minutes) and in the Ego-Organization (one rhythm in 45 minutes). Thus, in Craniosacral Therapy we have to deal with several rhythms, three to be exact, forming a trinity. Actually, we have to deal with several threefold functions—several trinities.

- We have the threefold soul: *feeling, will and thinking*.
- We have the threefold body which is the nervous system, the rhythmic system and the digestion/limb system.
- Then we have the threefold craniosacral rhythm: the shorter head rhythm, related to thinking, the longer heart rhythm related to feeling and the longest hip rhythm, related to will.
- There are three types of spiritual beings with whom to relate: The Father in the will, the Son in the feeling and the Holy Spirit in the thinking.
- There are three kinds of adversaries, the luciferic, the ahrimanic and the azuric.
- There are three spiritual bodies, the etheric body, the astral body and the 'ego organization'.

As in all spiritual work, we must first separate the three soul faculties (thinking, feeling and will) when we work with Craniosacral Therapy. Then we must be able to use them singly. In the body there are three craniosacral rhythms, one rhythm for the etheric body, one for the astral body and one for the ego-organisation. The etheric is stronger in the lower area of the body, the astral in the middle and the ego-organisation in the head. We must also consider that will is connected to the etheric, feeling to the astral and thinking to the 'I' or ego-organization.

We must use almost the same order and division in diagnosing. We should be in the thinking forces of the head when diagnosing the rhythm of the head. We should be in the will forces of the earth element or the hip area when diagnosing the rhythms of the hip, digestive or reproductive system. We should be in the feeling forces of the heart when diagnosing the rhythmic system of our feeling heart and rhythmic lungs.

In examining each rhythm, we should feel where the irregularities are, where there is something pathological. We then choose what rhythm to treat. In doing so we also choose what area to treat. We then choose whether to use the thinking, feeling or will as driving force in the treatment. In treatment, we use the respective forces we find in our own body. From the chest or heart, we feel and use the feeling rhythm to treat irregularities in the heart rhythm. From the head, we use the forces of our thinking to treat irregularities in the thinking rhythm. From the lower part of the body, we use the will powers to treat irregularities of the hip rhythm.

From the will, we use the will force to conquer the dominion of Ahriman. From the thinking, we use the thinking force to conquer the dominion of Lucifer. From the heart we feel reverence for the balancing and dissolving force of the Christ, for his love.

- In using thinking in the way here described, we open to the Imaginative world.
- In using feeling in the way here described, we open to the Inspirative world.
- In using will in the way here described, we open to the Intuitive world.

Then a lasting healing may occur, and no translocation of the disease.

Like cures (or frightens) like: a summary

A description of the similarities between herbal therapy, homeopathy, demon-pictures in churches and their relation to the Middle, the Christ

As described earlier in this book, it is a law in the etheric realm that everything is seen in reverse, as in a mirror. Everything has its opposite counterpart in the ethereal world. These relate to each other in the same way as the entangled particles within quantum physics, which are forever bound to each other in opposite directions.

Another deduction of this phenomenon is that 'like cures like'. Demons are frightened or driven away by their mirror image, following the same principle as Hahnemann's dictum, 'All plants or substances that show certain symptoms when given to a healthy person will cure the same symptoms in a diseased person.'

Example
On 30 May 2016, after giving a course in Italy, I visited Pisa. I went to see the Leaning Tower and realized immediately that there was something special about it. Tourist information informed me that there were many mysteries as to why it was built just there, why it was leaning and why it did not fall down completely. At the south side, the side from which the tower is leaning away, I observed spiritually that there is a huge etheric hole in the ground. I have only seen one other hole like this, and that was in Rishikesh in Northern India, just at the beginning of the river Ganges. These holes lead down to the ahrimanic forces of the earth. The people that built the tower in Pisa have placed a number of pillars around the tower at the first level (there are seven levels altogether, plus the bell tower at the top). On only two pillars can images of carved demons be seen: both face the demonic hole. The builders must have done this consciously. The tower leans away from the demonic hole, as if the demonic ahrimanic forces have pushed the tower away. I suppose that these forces also hold the tower in its place.

What is the significance and importance for the ahrimanic powers to have this tower as it is? According to my understanding, this tower was the first place where the new kind of free thought of the age showed itself in the genius of Galileo Galilei. The leaning of the tower made it possible for him to conceive the idea of dropping stones of different weight to the ground, and thus coming up with his theory that proved Aristotle wrong.

This act was the first action to free humanity from Scholastic thought. The ahrimanic forces needed this man, this tower and this place to free people from the grip of the Catholic Church and the old worldview, in order to direct people towards materialism. I believe Pisa was the main site of the ahrimanic attack on humankind in the sixteenth century. The history of the Church's grip on science through the writings of Aristotle and how the Renaissance freed the population of Europe from this grip is a long and exciting story, but it is not the task of this book to tell it! The building of the tower began in the twelfth century. However, the ahrimanic powers had prepared it for a long time.

How to avoid being ensnared and consumed by demonic entities—reflections on our times

As the reader will now understand, we all live our lives immersed in a spiritual reality of which we have no knowledge. We are subject to the influence of the three great adversaries, whose cosmic meaning is to give the human being freedom, which is otherwise unobtainable without the possibility of choosing out of our own free soul and spirit. However, these three powers have their own agenda, which is to obtain rulership over the human soul, to build their own kingdoms in which we as human beings will be the lowest hierarchy, the servant group, and not the tenth hierarchy of the angelic world, as has been intended from the beginning.

The goal of the adversaries may not be 'evil' as such and their intentions are not intrinsically bad, but they become so when they do not accept the divine order and goals.

- The luciferic powers want to make human beings utterly moral, without the ability to follow or fulfil temptation. They attempt this by trying to draw us away from the physical realm, where all temptation is to be found.
- The ahrimanic powers want to make sure that human beings are totally tied to the earth with a brain-bound intelligence. In order to do this, they have to hinder access to all the spiritual realms, where other laws apply. In this regard, it is important to know that the laws in this physical realm are only applicable to that realm. Each of the supersensible realms—etheric, astral, devachan and higher devachan—have their own distinct laws, different from each other and from those of the physical level. For instance, in the etheric realm,

the laws are completely different and often exactly opposite to those in the physical world. When we then consider that these different realities can be seen through four different types of awareness—physical, imaginative, inspirative and intuitive—and that in each of these four levels, each phenomenon can be considered in twelve different ways, it is obvious that Ahriman wants to keep us away from this confusing universe of spirit. He wants us to be earthbound, materialistic, intelligent inhabitants of the physical world, who then unfortunately and inevitably would end up in the Eighth Sphere—but this he keeps hidden in order to obtain his goal.

- In the present phase of Earth evolution, the Christ is supposed to give us 'I'-consciousness, and the azuric forces will fight against this with all their power. As both 'I'-consciousness and the Christ impulse are only in their early beginnings, the resistance from the Azuras will be much stronger in the future. The influence of Lucifer is already waning, whereas the might of Ahriman is at its highest whilst the strength of the Azuras is only at its beginning.

All of the adversaries will prevent us and keep us away from our 'normal' development as intended by the gods, and herein we can find one of the strongest and most effective weapons against the adversaries—the time-line and the memory of causal time.

Under the influence, or even the leadership, of these three great adversarial forces are hordes of ahrimanic, azuric and luciferic elementals of the most varied kinds. As we have seen, there are elementals connected to the four elements, to Wind, Fire, Water and Earth. There are elementals that were created alongside man at the creation of the Earth, and there are those that are created by our deeds, thoughts and feelings. There are ahrimanic and luciferic elementals existing throughout creation. There are also elementals connected to the creation of man himself, known by the names of goblins, elves and hidden people.

In the material realm, the elementals have promised the Father God to live in peace with each other,[*] especially the two main groups of elementals—ahrimanic and luciferic—who in themselves are polarized in that they want to fight each other. In the plant world and in the etheric realm, they have promised the same. That is why there are no diseases in the crystal or the etheric plant world. Also, in the animal world, the adversarial spirits have promised to live in peace but not necessarily in harmony.

---

[*] See Rudolf Steiner, *Geistige Zusammenhänge in der Gestaltung des menschlichen Organismus* (GA 218, Rudolf Steiner Verlag), p. 143ff. *Spirit as Sculptor of the Human Organism* (Rudolf Steiner Press, 2014).

Within the human realm, they have made the same promise, except as regards to human consciousness, the human 'I'. This exception also applies as far as the human I-consciousness reaches into the astral, etheric and physical bodies of both man, animal and plants and even the mineral world in the distant future. Here in the human consciousness, war rages between luciferic and ahrimanic forces. So now we are faced with the great question: how do we live in and survive this battle inside our consciousness? We have, to my knowledge and experience, four main ways of protection:

1. The time consciousness, in which the seven planetary epochs and their subdivisions are important.
2. The development of our spiritual sense organs, of which there are twelve.
3. Diseases, of which there are three groups of four, a totality of twelve, with cancer as an ultimate victory. This is an illusory victory for the adversaries but a real one for the human being.[*]
4. The balancing force and love of Christ, now appearing in the etheric, which is threefold. This force can also be found in nature (especially birds) and in the vast cosmos (stars).

We will now discuss how to use these four shields, how the adversaries try to eliminate them and even turn them against us, and how in the end we still have a good chance of winning and being able to save our spiritual life and our future as the intended 'tenth hierarchy'.

The consciousness of time

A good example of this has already been given in the development of my cancer therapy and how it eventually became ineffective, how this was remedied temporarily by my starting to activate the Middle or Christ Point, and how it stopped working again after 17 months.

At this stage, I started to gather my patients in a group, remembering that Christ told us that where two or three (or more) are gathered in his name he would be in their midst. Again, the treatment worked, but only for six months.

Then I added a protective shield to the group by introducing the 'time-cradle' (see illustration below), the U-shaped figure representing the cosmic timeline from Old Saturn to Vulcan. I was inspired in this by the protective work Rudolf Steiner had to do after he gave the lessons to the

_____

[*] See Rudolf Steiner, Ibid.

First Class of the School of Spiritual Science[*] in London in 1924. The thought behind this is the knowledge that the deeper wish of the adversaries is to pull human beings out of their timeline, to hinder their development throughout the time cycles, and prevent them from reaching the goal of their development.[†] Then, the healing and curing of cancer worked again as never before.

I will also add that included in the consciousness of time is the ability to remember, not through the blood as in old times, but through the soul and spirit. Dementia is another weapon used by the adversaries, as are the pharmaceutical products developed for treatment of other diseases. Medical science shows that the use of symptom-reducing medication will cause dementia to become more prevalent.

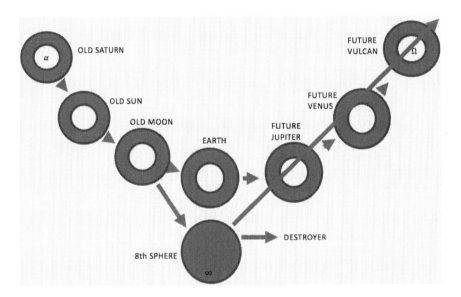

The twelve sense organs

This may be the area in which the ahrimanic forces are at their most cunning, as without etheric sense organs, we will have problems perceiving the Christ. At that time, in some hundreds of years, he will appear in the astral realm, and by then we should have developed astral sense organs to perceive him. The adversaries will also do their utmost to attempt to destroy these etheric organs and transfer them to luciferic sense

---

[*] For information on the School see Rudolf Steiner, *Constitution of the School of Spiritual Science*, Rudolf Steiner Press 2013.
[†] See Rudolf Steiner, *Philosophy, Cosmology and Religion* (GA 25), SteinerBooks 1998.

organs, just as the ahrimanic forces today work to create ahrimanic sense organs through the electromagnetic screens of TVs and smartphones, and thus also counteract our normal etheric sense organs. Today we already see how, in our exposure to virtual reality, Lucifer and Ahriman have started to create their own senses.

This is so important today that I will elaborate further. I would conjecture that most people believe that the explosion of technological advances has been the herald of an era of profound change. With the push of a few buttons, anything and everything can be found, researched, bought and sold. In addition, our ability to connect immediately with one another through social media has morphed the concept of the written word. Language has now taken on a divisiveness of monumental proportions, as the 'instant word' has assumed the role of becoming the most effective weapon since the invention of the gun. Therefore, it is no wonder that the existence of electronic technology has also created an effective tool for the blossoming of adversarial forces—the exact methodology through which Ahriman, as the primary sinister force, can manipulate the devices of this technology to gain control over the future of humanity. His major access point is through the portals created by our sense organs

Rudolf Steiner has described thoroughly the existence of twelve senses.[*] He claimed that each of these faculties act as openings or portals to both the physical, etheric and astral aspects of both man and the cosmos in which we live. Each sense is connected to one of the divine beings of the first hierarchy, expressed in each of the twelve signs of the zodiac. In this way, they can be viewed as a twelvefold entity.

In Steiner's description of the human being, he categorizes our invisible anatomy in various ways. First, he divides us into four layers, consisting of our physical, etheric, astral and 'I' sheaths. However, this concept of a fourfold being can be further described as having both seven, or even nine, levels, if one also considers our spiritual future as including the higher levels, named Buddhi, Manas and Atma.

Ultimately our higher selves, as well as all of creation, are governed by a primary trinity of the powerful soul faculties of thinking, feeling and will. They represent the fundamental processes in which our cosmos is organized and developed and weave themselves into all aspects of creation. This trinity encompasses the entire cosmos, the divine angelic hierarchies, as well as the 'sub-natural' world of spiritual beings such as elves, hidden people and other elementals. This latter aspect of our universe can be seen

---

[*] See lecture by Rudolf Steiner, 'The Twelve Human Senses', Berlin, 20 June 1916.

with the spiritual eye as an upside down reality of the physical world (or perhaps it could be our world that is upside down). In this way, one can imagine that our feet would make contact with their reverse image beneath the spiritual earth.

The three cosmic forces play a role in every aspect of our lives. In anthroposophical medicine, there are the three fundamental poles: the nerve-sensory system (thinking), the rhythmic system (feeling) and the metabolic/muscular/skeletal system (will).[*] However, it is of paramount importance that we understand that this template can also be applied to the twelve senses. This is relevant particularly when we are considering the steps towards spiritual initiation known as Imagination (the four physical senses of touch, life, movement and orientation), Inspiration (the four soul-senses of smell, taste, temperature and sight), and Intuition (the four spiritual senses of hearing, speech, thought and perception of the 'I' of others).

The senses described by Steiner are extremely complex formations as they exhibit both an outward and inward direction of flow. For example, the eyes which perceive the cosmos, are sending an outward etheric stream enabling them to also receive an inward flow of information from what they are viewing. It is a general spiritual rule that any movement automatically creates a counter-movement, even involving time.

The twelve senses are also in the luciferic, ahrimanic, and human karmic doppelgängers. These three entities employ the senses in a unique way. The human karmic doppelgänger uses the physical sense organs as we use them in the material world. However, the ahrimanic and luciferic doppelgängers create their own mirror images of these structures. The templates that ahrimanic forces utilize are situated deeper within the physical body, while the luciferic templates are more superficial, infil-trating the astral sheath. For example, in the eye, the ahrimanic sense organs lie about one centimetre behind the material optic structure while the luciferic sense organs are in front of the eye. I perceive the ahrimanic structure with my clairvoyant ability as a greyish structure, similar to a tin plate.

These structures are also activated and developed by viewing electronic screens. From this information, it can be surmised that there are actually three aspects of each of these sense organs. If one considers all twelve sense organs and combines the fact that all these senses are employed by three doppelgängers (including ourselves), and that each organ is involved in both an outgoing and an ingoing stream, we come to the conclusion that

[*] Rudolf Steiner and Ita Wegman, *Extending Practical Medicine*, Rudolf Steiner Press 2000.

we are actually dealing with 72 qualities that must be considered when understanding sensory function. Note that all twelve senses can create a spiritual faculty. For example, if the spiritual eye is developed, we refer to that ability as clairvoyance.

The first sense I will discuss is the eye, the foundation of sight and also central to imagination and clairvoyance. Regarding the eye as a physical organ, I have observed that when viewing a living object, especially in nature, the inhabitants of higher spiritual hierarchies are also sharing the observation. I have also found that the sense organs with little or no fat, such as the eye, have a stronger affinity to the etheric. However, when one is observing the screen of a cell phone, the observations are intertwined with another reality, where colours diminish and ahrimanic forces dominate.

Regarding the effect of the presence of the effects of Lucifer and Ahriman on our sense organ of sight, whether we are observing the results of these demonic influences on the nature of the physical world or on the 'sub-nature' of the virtual electronic world, I find that both demons can thrive on the latter. This includes the Internet, artificial light, LED displays, computer monitors and cell phones.[*] Because the adversaries are able to take part in this 'underworld' via electronics, handwriting is a safer alternative for communication as it is under the domain of the angels.

The strength of these doppelgängers is woven into sensory observations. Paul Emberson claims that the use of computers stimulates the adversarial forces' stronghold on our existence. For example, if one views a movie, one will actually strengthen the ahrimanic doppelgänger's visual sense organ. As mentioned above, this eye is grey and large, similar in appearance to a tin plate. In 1917, Steiner addresses his concern about attending a movie theatre.[†] He describes that the eyes of those watching a movie take on the sense organs of Ahriman. An interesting inference to such an eye in literature is in the famous Ibsen play, *Peer Gynt*. A surgery is described where a slit is made in the eye by the adversarial forces to deceive the person into thinking that everything he sees is beautiful, in order to assure his marriage with the troll king's daughter.

The second sense I would like to discuss is that of feeling. The related

---

[*] See Paul Emberson, *From Gondhishapur to Silicon Valley*, Etheric Dimensions Press 2005.

[†] See *Cosmic and Human Metamorphosis*, Lecture 4: 'While people are sitting at the cinema, what they see there does not make its way into the ordinary faculty of perception, it enters a deeper, more material stratum than we usually employ for our perception. A person becomes etherically "goggle-eyed" at the cinema; he develops eyes like those of a seal, only much larger—I mean larger etherically. This works in a materializing way, not only upon what he has in his consciousness, but upon its deepest sub-consciousness.'

organ to this sense at the physical level is the skin. My observations regarding this organ date back to well before my understanding of anthroposophy. During the first years of my veterinary studies at Oslo University, I spent some time between classes observing the tourists, especially those who were overweight. I saw, with my spiritual eye that, in many of those people, the skin was in front of a withdrawn etheric sheath. The fatty tissue was, in a way, hanging loose, out of the etheric field. In this way, the effect of the sense organ allowing clairsentience was diminished. In other words, weight can have an effect on supersensory feeling. Therefore, when a person goes on a weight reduction programme, it may be possible for them to develop their spiritual sense of touch, as the etheric sheath expands in an outward direction, thus diminishing the stranglehold of Ahriman and Lucifer on this particular sense organ. This might be why Christ fasted as he resisted the temptations of these demons during his 40 days in the desert. Perhaps being thinner allowed him to attain a higher level of spirituality.

When the physical sense organ of the skin is involved, as well as its luciferic and ahrimanic templates, we should understand how Rudolf Steiner described clairvoyance as a relationship between the physical body, etheric body and astral body, especially when the spiritual bodies are outside the physical form. For example, during the time of Atlantis, the etheric sheath of the head was outside its physical counterpart. In this way, Atlanteans were clairvoyant and able to observe the etheric world. However, if the etheric body is within the physical body, the supersensible sense organs become dulled.

From the above it would seem that the ahrimanic and luciferic sense organs are developing in synchronization with our growing love of technology, especially over the past 20 years. As Goethe wrote, that the sun created the need for our human eyes, so will the existence of virtual media and electronic devices create the need for an ahrimanic eye.

I have observed that children are developing a special affinity for understanding and utilizing such devices, as the 'double eye' becomes more sophisticated. The healthy spiritual forces, in contrast, avoid such devices, creating a dissolution of unhealthy social connections among the populace.

An even more sinister connotation lies in the inability for us to advance our goal towards spiritual initiation through the process of Imagination, Inspiration, and Intuition. Therefore, we must proceed with caution to limit electronic communications in our daily life by restraining ourselves from using email, Facebook and other such forms of social media. Our soul life, etheric life and our physical bodies depend on it. We must protect our future now, whether it be for our children but also for the future of the spirit of humanity as a whole.

Disease

Although every disease is created by the ahrimanic and the luciferic forces, what we experience as a disease is actually the healing of the 'real' disease. This needs some further explanation. A body in balance is a healthy body. It is ruled by the balanced forces of both the luciferic and the ahrimanic, with the Christ in the balancing Middle. If we weaken an organ by our eating habits, or weaken the etheric by our thoughts or the astral body by our feelings, in such a way that either of the adversaries gains an upper hand, the connected organs will suffer imbalance, disease or pain.

The disease symptoms in themselves are to be considered the healing of the imbalance,[*] a healing through the conscious soul or 'I' function. In this way, the adversaries are rendered helpless in overthrowing the human soul and are then directed towards helping the body to restore the balance.

Modern drugs do not do this, they just make the symptoms disappear, and in this way all modern medicines will leave the stronger adversary just as strong or even stronger. In cancer this is most obvious, as this disease is a cooperation of the luciferic and the ahrimanic forces, and as such they will both become more powerful from modern radiation and chemotherapy.[†]

Christ in the Etheric

Between 1911 and 1925, Rudolf Steiner repeatedly predicted that the most important happening in the twentieth century was to be the appearance of Christ in the etheric realm. This appearance must be found by human beings as well as by all the beneficial elemental beings, or humankind will face many difficult times. Personally, I have observed that

---

[*] Rudolf Steiner talks about how we lay the foundation for illnesses in previous lives and the role of pain as a corrective: 'When we fall into the power of Lucifer, there immediately intervenes a counteraction by powers antagonistic to the luciferic powers. These exercise an opposing force, whereby the luciferic influence may be actually driven out of us. And it is these forces, opponents of the luciferic powers, which add pain to the process resulting from Lucifer's influence. Thus, if the luciferic powers are evil, we must regard pain as something which is given us by benevolent forces, because through pain we escape from the clutches of these evil powers, and do not succumb to them again.' (*Manifestations of Karma*, Lecture seven, Hamburg, 22 May 1919, Rudolf Steiner Press 2000.)

[†] See Are Thoresen, *Spiritual Medicine* (CreateSpace, 2018).

this Christ force in nature can be experienced by listening to the birds singing. Birdsong is in its essence etheric. This song also activates the finer etheric streams, especially in and around the heart, enabling us to develop the conscious part (the remaining six petals) of the heart chakra, and then making it possible to conceive Christ in our hearts. Interestingly, the Waffen-SS was 'trained' by putting needles into birds, to make them suffer as much as possible.

The return of Christ in the etheric was counteracted by all three realms of adversaries, especially with the help of the Azuras in the appearance of Hitler. After World War Two, the work of the adversaries continued with the destruction of fairytales (Walt Disney), free 'love' (casual sex, hippies), drugs (hallucinogenic, opening of hexagonal portals), electronic music (amplifiers), the 'ahrimanization' of the twelve senses and the use of pharmaceutical medicines that only treat symptomatically.

Summary

Listen to live music and birdsong, avoid electronic music and media, become more aware of and look at the stars, contact friends face-to-face, don't use too much pharmaceutical medicine, don't get overweight and be conscious of our goal, destiny and progression through the timeline.

Addendum

Spiritual beings and drugs

Encountering positive and negative entities induced by psychedelic substances during travels in other dimensional realities
Whilst I do not condone the taking of illegal or illicit substances, what I describe below is a factual description of the result of taking such substances and the dangers inherent therein.

Many people that have used drugs encounter spiritual entities, and this could be one of the reasons we believe such entities to be mere hallucinations. However, this is not so! Psychotropic plants and substances open doorways or portals into a *real* spiritual world. This doorway, once opened, can be travelled both ways, thus allowing entities living in the spiritual world (both good and bad) to invade and enter us or to be invited in, and also for us to enter the spiritual realm opened by the use of specific substances or plants.

Therefore, we need to be strong and conscious enough to defend our soul and spirit against alien influences, and keep our Self, our 'I', free of such entities that are harmful to us. The entities that have our wellbeing at heart want us to develop as spiritual beings and are much less aggressive/invasive. Instead, they await an invitation.

Rudolf Steiner's whole philosophy, in a nutshell, is based on balancing the adverse powers of Lucifer and Ahriman through cosmic Christ Consciousness. Thus, in order to be clear about who and what it is we are dealing with, we must understand the spirit world, know its inhabitants and be able to protect ourselves should we meet undesirable influences. All portals or doorways to the spiritual worlds are 'personal' and must be conquered by the conscious self to become an everlasting property of the human spirit.

The knowledge that other dimensions are inhabited by spirits/entities is very important when we evaluate, describe and understand the workings of natural (or synthetic) psychotropic plants and hallucinogens used to enter into the spiritual worlds.

How does a hallucinogenic/psychotropic substance work within the human body?
As described, hallucinogenic substances open doorways, portals or tunnels that lead into the spiritual world. These portals can take us to situations where we encounter both good and bad entities, spirits and demons.

Through these tunnels we enter (or see) into the spiritual world, and as such we can learn much. What happens to us when we travel dimensionally and what we learn depends upon our ability to 'fill' these tunnels with our consciousness and to be able to navigate in the spiritual world. If we are not properly prepared, do not have the right mindset, or our will is weak, the opposite may happen. The malevolent powers of the spiritual world may influence us more than we are aware of and may attach themselves to us or even take possession of us in some way. They may drain us of energy, make us ill, enter our thoughts and cause havoc in our lives, depression being just one aspect of this.

This is the understated danger of using hallucinogenic or psychotropic substances, which many are unaware of, especially those who do not take the spiritual world seriously. We need to be careful that we don't open ourselves to the darker spirits and allow them into our being. That is why in traditional cultures psychotropic plants or medicines were only taken in the company of an experienced shaman or guide, someone who had good other-dimensional navigational skills. It is equally necessary to be in a harmonious place, both physically and mentally, and to understand who you are and why you are doing what you are doing. That said, one must also have the resources to recognize and deal with any negative entities, should they be met. We must protect ourselves from these malevolent demonic spirits that can enter and travel all the way into the heart. This protection can only be effectively maintained by the help of our own consciousness.

Different plants or substances open up to different spheres or compartments in the spiritual world:

- LSD opens to spirits beyond the physical realm.
- DMT opens to the spirits of the Eighth Sphere, which are especially insect-like.
- Ayahuasca opens to the plant spirits of South America.
- Iboga opens to African nature-gods.
- Cocaine opens to the ahrimanic higher spirit (of America).
- Opium opens to lower luciferic spirits (of the Orient).
- Marihuana opens to higher luciferic spirits (of the Orient).
- Mushrooms open to the ahrimanic spirits to be found in nature (local spirits).
- Alcohol opens to lower ahrimanic spirits (of the whole world).

Poltergeists

Unfortunately, I have had a long history with poltergeists. Throughout my life, I have suffered the 'jokes' from these spirits, which must surely be considered to be demons. They interfere in the physical world, they change the physical world, they interact without the acceptance or conscious will of the people involved, although it seems that they may also accidentally perform good deeds.

Example 1
I was living at a Camphill village called Vidaråsen, situated in Vestfold, Norway. On a Saturday, the family with whom I was living prepared a 'Bible evening'. I was asked to wear a suit for this occasion but did not have one. I was only 21 years old, so I borrowed one from my father. I brought the suit to my room and put it on the bed. The room was small with only one window, one door, one bed and one sink. I put the suit on the bed and looked away for five seconds. When I looked back it was gone, and it never showed up again. I lied to my father and told a story of how I had lost it, a story he could believe. If I had told the truth, he would have thought I was mad.

Example 2
I was returning from Zürich with my wife. We had a long stopover in Amsterdam and decided to go sightseeing. We put our suitcases in a big storage locker, put in our money and out came the relevant ticket. I took it and gave it to my wife so she could keep it safe in her little purse. I thought she received the ticket, and she thought I took it back. Midway between the two of us, it disappeared. We did not understand that until later, when we came to collect the suitcases. After five minutes of arguing over which one of us had the ticket, we both searched our pockets and every conceivable place for perhaps 20 minutes. No ticket was found. We contacted a security guard and after another 20 minutes he managed to open the locker and we continued our travel. On arriving home, we unlocked the entrance door, went into the living room, and there, in the middle of the table was the ticket, not crumpled or creased in the slightest.

Example 3
I had put my wallet on the living room table (the same table where the ticket showed up in the previous example). I put on my jacket to go to town. Just as I went to grab my wallet, it was gone. The table was tidy, with only a few things on it. The wallet had really disappeared. I had to borrow some money from my wife and went in to town. On arriving home, the wallet was there, lying in the middle of the table.

Example 4
I had laid my hairbrush on the glass shelf above the sink in the bathroom. The next morning, I went to brush my hair, but the brush was gone. It did not reappear, so I bought a new one. One morning, six months later, it reappeared on the bathroom shelf, all by itself.

Example 6
I was walking in a forest with my wife when suddenly I saw a beautiful feather lying on the ground in front of me. I took it up and gave it to her. She took it and put it in her rucksack. When we came home, it was gone. The following night I dreamt that an old North American Indian told me the feather was meant for me, and that I should not give it away. He told me I would get another chance. After a month or so, I went down into the cellar to fetch a backpack that had been hanging there for two years. The feather was there in the backpack.

Example 7
I had planned to travel from Oslo airport to Switzerland. I had my passport in the inner pocket of my jacket. To check that the passport was there, I looked at it several times on the train to the airport. When I arrived at the airport security desk, the passport was gone. I looked through all my pockets several times, but it was gone. I returned home as I could not travel without the passport. When I came home, the passport was once again in my pocket.

What are Poltergeists?

This is a tricky question to answer. As stated previously, spirits are not allowed to interfere with human free will. If they have turned towards the dark side and joined the demonic realm, however, it seems that they may do whatever they choose.

Spirits that interfere with the free human will are defined as demonic. Mostly, they are of the demonic kind, but sometimes it seems to me that they are serving a higher purpose, as when I was given the feather.

My meeting with a man who was investigating the phenomenon of poltergeists

I was aged 21 and was at a meeting in Oslo. During the meeting, I felt hungry and left the room to buy some bananas from a kiosk. I went in and purchased the bananas. As I was leaving to return to the meeting, an elderly man on my left side suddenly addressed me asking, 'Has anything of yours disappeared lately?' I was surprised, because I happened to be in the middle of a period when poltergeists were especially active. 'Yes,' I replied. He continued, 'You see, I am investigating the phenomenon of poltergeists, and am gathering as many stories as possible about this subject. An hour ago, a voice told me to come to this kiosk and address the man on my right and ask him about poltergeists.' I was stunned, and we agreed to go to his home to talk more about this phenomenon. I left the meeting and spent the rest of the day with him. He told me a lot about the poltergeist phenomena. I will briefly share his knowledge:

1. There are as many people who receive things as people who lose the same things.
2. The people that receive things are usually in need of what they received, such as money, food or other items. Some things that disappear turn up again. They are borrowed for a short while only. Sometimes it seems that the poltergeists just make fun of you. It seems that there is some sort of cosmic 'Robin Hood' who takes from the rich and gives to the needy poor.

Therefore, I guess I did not need the suit but somebody else did. The ticket in Amsterdam, however, was just 'fun'. These actions are definitely carried out by demonic spirits, but I do not know what sort of spirits or demons they are.

Conclusion

Writing this book has been a very difficult task, especially as most of my friends do not believe that demons exist. I would have been ridiculed had I talked to them and tried to explain its contents. However, I believe that now is the time to speak about demons; in fact, the time is overdue.

Ahriman and Lucifer want to take over the rulership of both the material and the spirit world, and it is vital that they be hindered. The battle will be fought through our *thinking*, our *feeling* and our *will*.

Ahriman, Lucifer and their helping legions of demons, work on earth, in our bodies, in our souls and in our spirits. They cause disease, materialism, atheism and immorality.

If demons take over the three soul faculties (thinking, feeling and will) of humanity, the human race will be lost for eternity. Therefore, knowledge of demons, the soul faculties and the Christ are of crucial importance today. Such knowledge will work as a healing impulse in humanity, opening the way for Christ and his higher angels. These are the only forces that can counteract demonic power. Such knowledge will help us to conquer and release these demons. The key protective/counteracting force against demonic power is the human incorporation of the Christ Consciousness in thinking, feeling and will.

Today, it is equally difficult to talk about Christ Consciousness as it is to talk about the existence of demons. The name of Christ is devalued and scorned, both in the general population and in alternative circles. This is due to the misdeeds of many senior clerics over the centuries. Sinful clerics have behaved in diametric opposition to what Christ Jesus taught. Their misdeeds have created massive scandals and led to the consequent alienation of good Christians and especially of young people.

In my opinion, it must be emphasized that the Christ Essence, the cosmic force that incarnated in Jesus of Nazareth, is the only force that can counteract the destructive forces emanating from ahrimanic and luciferic demons. In my knowledge of Tantrism, Hinduism, Buddhism and many other spiritual movements, I have not found any deeper understanding of this unique force.

Afterword

Many people will be upset greatly by three words—demons, spiritual and Christology—in the title of this book. These words will cause many others to question the sanity of the author, Are Simeon Thoresen.

Psychic ability—the sixth sense—is a primitive sense inherent in all living things. Its basic purpose in animals and people is to aid survival, viz. to sense danger, find water, food, shelter, missing young, etc. Because urbanized people have lost touch with nature to a great extent, their psychic sense has atrophied through lack of use, but it is still there and can be cultivated and rekindled by proper training.

Genius is a rare commodity that few of us attain. I see the colour-magic painted by Van Gogh, hear the music-magic of Beethoven, imagine touching the exquisite bronze of Rodin's *Thinker*. I revere their work but know that I can never create such beauty. So, it is with Are's psychic skills.

Are has been a friend for more than 20 years. My initial impressions were that he was either a conman or mentally deluded, living in a world of make-believe. However, having spent time with him, seeing him work, talking to some of his human patients and animal owners and reading his papers and books on healing, I now see him as a man of many talents, a veterinary colleague, acupuncturist, homeopath, naturopath, psychic, seer, gifted healer and seeker-of-truth.

Stress is at record levels today. Rates of marriage breakup, antisocial behaviour, mental disorders, psychoactive medication, drug addiction, alcoholism, criminality, self-harm and suicide are very high. Could this be because many people do not believe in a Supreme God, the Great Healer and Creator of all that exists? Could this be because they deny the possibility of evil discarnate spirits invading their body-mind-spirit?

Non-believers deny the reality of an afterlife, viz. that the human spirit is immortal. They may accept that Jesus Christ was a great teacher but deny that he was the God-Essence in human form. They do not believe in angels or demons. Such people are unlikely to read this book. That will be their loss, for there is much to learn about themselves and their physical, mental and spiritual health within these pages.

We all have our individual strengths and weaknesses. *We all harbour dark passengers to some extent.* Few will master Are's ability to see and sense the spirit world as he does, but if you are a thinker and seeker of truth, I urge you to read this book and to try his methods. Some of them may work for you. If you have serious health issues, especially mental/spiritual issues, put your trust in the infinite love of the Creator / Great Healer / Christ-Essence. Believe that those Almighty Powers can release your demons.

So be it!

Phil Rogers, Dublin, Ireland
22 August, 2016

Acknowledgements

Thanking my colleagues and those who have inspired me

Man does not live alone in the world.

This book would have been impossible to write without the inspiration and advice from close friends and colleagues:

Dr Med. Vet. Markus Steiner, Dr Med. Vet. Phillip Rogers, Tierheil-praktiker Corinne Dettmer, Cand. Agronom Asbjørn Lavoll, Philosopher DrPh. Hans Kolstad and Artist Lizz Daniels.

Thank you to all.

A note from the publisher

For more than a quarter of a century, **Temple Lodge Publishing** has made available new thought, ideas and research in the field of spiritual science.

Anthroposophy, as founded by Rudolf Steiner (1861-1925), is commonly known today through its practical applications, principally in education (Steiner-Waldorf schools) and agriculture (biodynamic food and wine). But behind this outer activity stands the core discipline of spiritual science, which continues to be developed and updated. True science can never be static and anthroposophy is living knowledge.

Our list features some of the best contemporary spiritual-scientific work available today, as well as introductory titles. So, visit us online at **www.templelodge.com** and join our emailing list for news on new titles.

If you feel like supporting our work, you can do so by buying our books or making a direct donation (we are a non-profit/ charitable organisation).

office@templelodge.com

✵ TEMPLE LODGE

For the finest books of Science and Spirit